BIBLE LANDS MUSEUM JERUSALEM

GUIDE TO THE COLLECTION

R. SIRKIS PUBLISHERS LTD.

BIBLE LANDS MUSEUM JERUSALEM

Produced by R. Sirkis Publishers Ltd.
Graphic Design: Larry Ziegler

Photo Credits:
Katherine Dempsey Amrani: 126.
Brian Boyle: 10 (Bottom), 21, 47 (Bottom).
H. Fleury: 38 (Top).
David Harris: 15, 28, 32, 33, 37, 61, 65, 69, 77, 78, 79, 82, 84, 91, 94, 95 (Bottom), 98, 108, 109, 112, 113, 114, Front Cover.
Avraham Hay: 11, 14, 18, 19, 22, 29, 42, 44, 49, 52, 53, 63, 64, 76, 86, 88, 93, 99, 105, 106, 115, 116.
Hans Hinz: 101, 110, 120.
Icons Ltd. Multimedia Productions, Jerusalem: 25.
David Loggie: 23, 57.
Zev Radovan: 30, 31, 36, 39, 40, 41, 45, 48, 56 (Top), 60, 72, 73, 74, 90, 92, 95 (Top), 102, 103, 104, 111, 117, 121, 124, 125, 127, Back Cover.
J. Robert: 34.
Bill Robertson: 10 (Top), 56 (Bottom), 87, 118.
Dietrich Widmer: 20, 26, 47 (Top), 46, 50, 80, 123.

Illustration Credits:
Michael Berger: 38 (Bottom).
Dalit Weinblatt: 4.

EDITOR: Lindsey Taylor-Guthartz
TYPESET: Daatz, Jerusalem

Second Edition, printed in Israel, 1994
All Rights Reserved. No part of this publication may be reproduced in any form without written permission.
® Bible Lands Museum Jerusalem
P.O.Box 4670 Jerusalem 91046
® R. Sirkis Publishers Ltd.
P.O.Box 3561 Ramat-Gan 52135

ISBN 965-387-031-9

Front Cover:
Painted wooden coffin (detail); Egypt, Meir, ca. 1963-1875 B.C.E.
Back Cover:
Family, baked clay; Syria, ca. 2000 B.C.E.

TABLE OF CONTENTS

THE ANCIENT NEAR EAST: LANDS OF THE BIBLE

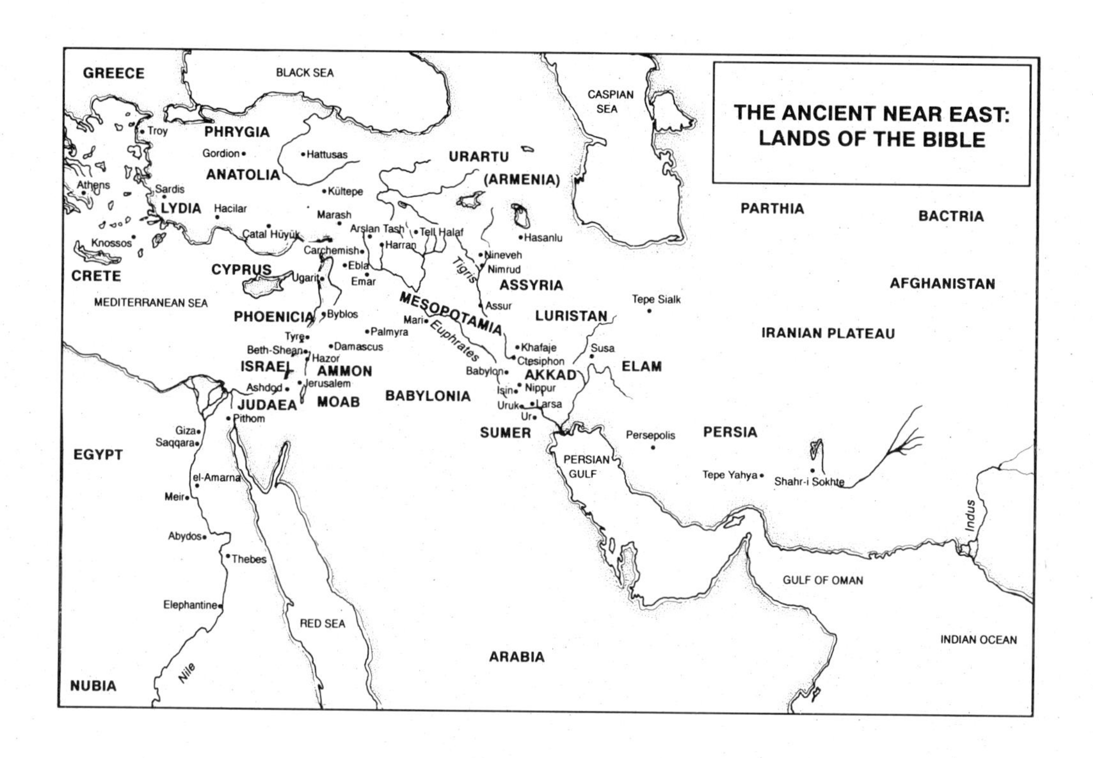

INTRODUCTION

The Bible Lands Museum Jerusalem houses one of the world's most unusual collections of ancient artefacts, illustrating the civilisations of the biblical period. Initially one man's dream, this museum was created by Dr. Elie Borowski, a former ancient Near Eastern art dealer and scholar, who carefully collected the 4,000 objects in the museum over a period of nearly 50 years.

The museum is designed to give the visitor a glimpse of the world of the Bible. The exhibition highlights the relationship between the spiritual and physical worlds, following in the footsteps of man's quest for the transcendental, and covers the initial stages of the three great monotheistic religions: Judaism, Christianity and Islam.

This guide was written to lead you through the permanent exhibition and to highlight outstanding and interesting features. It will help you to understand the objects and the stories and myths that many of them illustrate.

These objects were made, used and valued by people long ago. They were part of everyday life, were used in religious rituals, and demonstrate the origins of communication and urbanisation.

We can better understand the history of the land of Israel when we look at it in relation to the influences that affected Israel during the biblical period. Just as no man is an island, neither is any culture, particularly in the ebb-and-flow of the Near East. Israel, a small country at the crossroads of the mainstream of the ancient world, was influenced by the Babylonians, the Egyptians, the Phoenicians, the Aramaeans and the Greeks in turn. Each of these cultures left its imprint on the customs, concepts and material culture of ancient Israel.

The Bible Lands Museum Jerusalem illustrates the cultures of all the peoples mentioned in the Bible - from Egypt eastward across the Fertile Crescent to Afghanistan, and from Nubia northwards to the Caucasian mountains. You will learn about the Philistines and the Aramaeans, the Hittites, the Phoenicians and the Persians. The Mesopotamians, the pyramid builders of ancient Egypt and the ancient Phoenicians are no longer with us, but the Bible and its teachings became the basis of western civilisation and have shaped its history for centuries.

The Museum is arranged chronologically. We have chosen to illustrate the changes which took place in different lands simultaneously, enhanced by wall maps placed throughout the galleries.

The Museum has recently developed a very modern, hi-tech method of bringing history to life. In the Gallery of Symbolic Communications, Gallery 3, you will discover the most innovative and exciting new interactive multimedia computer retrieval program, designed to explore one of the earliest forms of communication: cylinder and stamp seals. The multimedia seal program, SEALS: A Journey in Time, enables you to view a seal in a variety of ways. You can "impress" or "roll out" the seal and learn about its origins - cultural, historical, religious, geographical, mythological, geological - and the biblical quotations that mention seals.

Biblical quotations are placed throughout the galleries, referring to the periods and cultures from which these artefacts came. These quotations are not intended to imply that the exhibits you see before you are the actual objects described in the Bible, but since they come from the periods and civilisations mentioned there, their juxtaposition with the biblical quotations adds another dimension to our understanding of the world of the Bible.

We hope that this guide will have enriched your understanding and given you a deeper insight into the exhibition at the Bible Lands Museum Jerusalem.

Scholarly studies on the collection are available in the previous publications: O. Muscarella (ed.), *Ladders to Heaven*, Toronto, 1981, R. Merhav (ed.), *Treasures of the Bible Lands*, Tel Aviv, 1987 and *Collezione Anatolica di Borowski, Studia Mediterranea III*, Pavia, 1981.

We are most grateful to everyone who has contributed their advice, knowledge, expertise and efforts to the preparation of this guide.

THE FOUNDERS AND THE HISTORY OF THE COLLECTION

When one day late in the autumn of 1943 Dr. Elie Borowski bought his first cylinder seal, he never suspected that he had set his feet on a path which would bring him to Jerusalem, to a museum built to house the work of a lifetime. That single seal is now one of the fourteen hundred seals and almost four thousand objects in his collection.

Born in Warsaw in 1913, Dr. Borowski studied at the Mir Yeshiva and went on to study for the rabbinate at the Collegio Rabbinico Italiano in Florence. At that time he became enamoured of the art and history of the ancient Near East and decided to devote his life to studying it.

At the Pontifical Biblical Institute in Rome he learnt to read cuneiform and specialised in early Sumerian writings.

Just before the outbreak of the Second World War, while studying in Paris in August 1939, Dr. Borowski enlisted with a unit of Jewish volunteers of the French army to fight the Nazis. As a military internee in Switzerland, he worked part-time for the Museum of Art and History in Geneva.

The Geneva museum had a collection of Mesopotamian seals and some cuneiform tablets. He began to publish them, first in learned articles and then in his book, *Cylindres et Cachets Orientaux*. After receiving his doctoral degree from the University of Geneva, he was invited as a Lady Davis Fellow to the Royal Ontario Museum in Toronto as a research associate.

Devastated by the loss of his family during the Holocaust, Borowski felt there was no point in art and music, poetry and literature if they could not provide people with the moral courage to withstand injustice and barbarism. The need for an awakening of moral and spiritual values contained in the Bible gradually developed into a lifetime goal. He believed the most effective way to reach this goal was to assemble a collection of artefacts from the Lands of the Bible that would confirm and elucidate the riches of the biblical world with its ethics and spirituality.

His first acquisition in Geneva in 1943 set the tone of his collection: a cylinder seal engraved in ancient Hebrew letters with the name "Ṣhallum," which he thought referred to Shallum son of Yavesh, who had usurped the throne of the kingdom of Israel for a short time in 741 B.C.E.

Over the years, Borowski has put together a choice collection of objects. Each seal, relief or figurine documents some event or person, or interprets some story or custom of our ancient past.

In 1968, objects from this collection were shown in New York in an exhibition marking the twentieth anniversary of the State of Israel.

In 1976, the Lands of the Bible Archaeology Foundation was established in Toronto, and in 1979 the exhibition "Ladders to Heaven" was shown at the Royal Ontario Museum. A selection of objects was published in 1981 in a book entitled *Ladders to Heaven*, named after the cylinder seal (on display in the Sumerian Temple — Gallery 6) which depicts the gods climbing a ladder to build a tower, linking earth and heaven, like the ladder of Jacob's vision in Genesis 28:2.

In 1982 Elie Borowski and Batya Gamiel Weiss were married. They devoted themselves entirely to the fulfillment of Elie's dream, the establishment of the Bible Lands Museum in Jerusalem.

In 1985 the ground-breaking ceremony was held on the site where the museum stands today. On May 11, 1992 the Bible Lands Museum Jerusalem opened for Israel and the world.

Elie and Batya Borowski are grateful to the many friends, supporters and the excellent team that make up the staff of the Bible Lands Museum Jerusalem, who have helped bring this museum to its realisation, and who actively support its future.

MUSEUM FLOOR PLAN

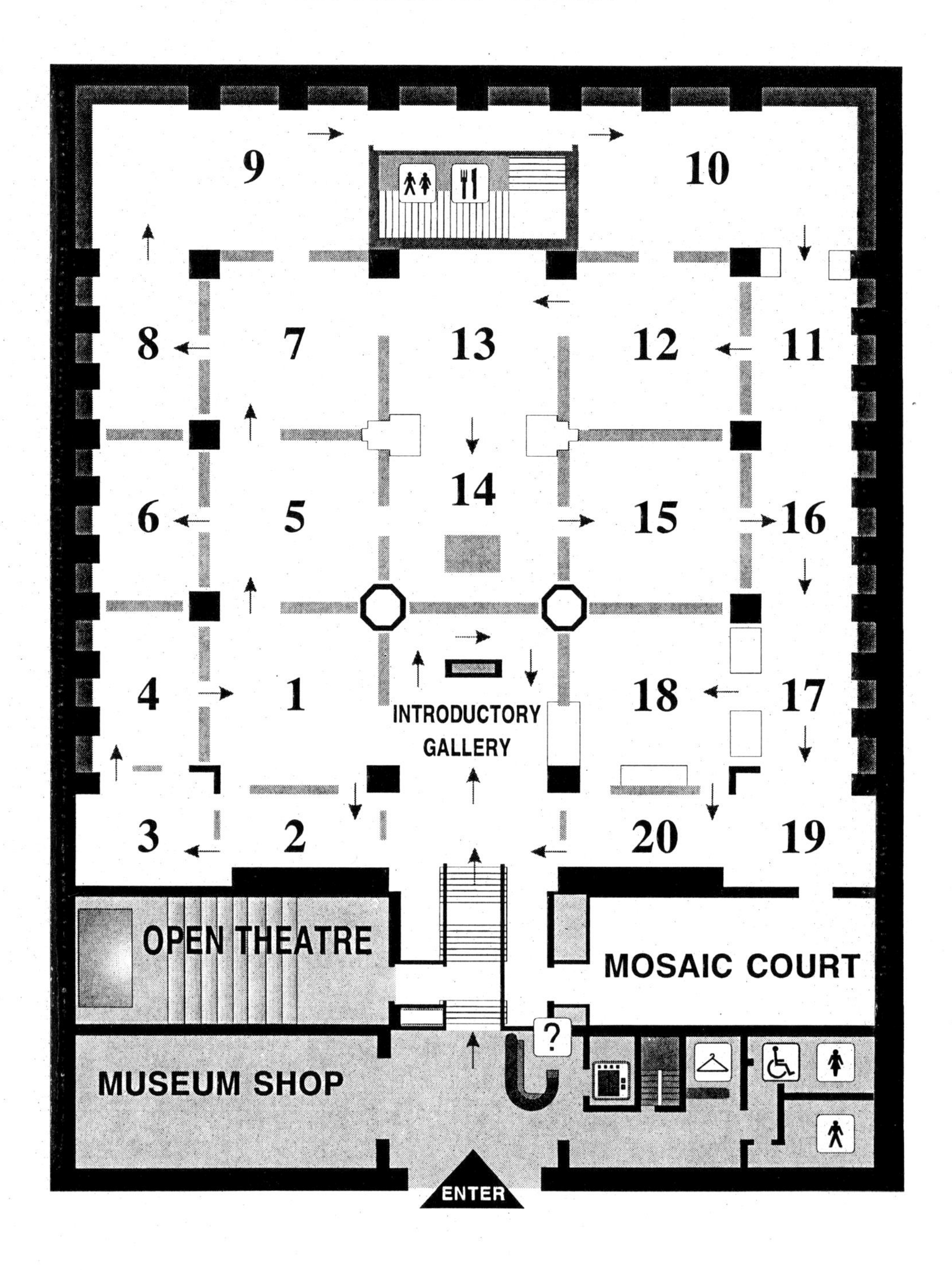

INTRODUCTORY GALLERY

THE FAMILY OF MAN

These are the families of the sons of Noah, after their generations, in their nations; and of these were the nations divided in the earth after the flood.
(Genesis 10:32)

In its very first chapters, the Bible lays the foundations for the concept of the unity of humankind, teaching us that all people are descended from Adam, who was created by God. We are thus all brothers and sisters, since we are all sons and daughters of Adam and Eve. Other ancient peoples also realized this unity. Although in their trading and travelling they met people who dressed differently, spoke unintelligible languages and worshipped strange gods, they must have noticed that these foreigners were not so very different — they too felt hunger and thirst, joy and sadness, love and anger. Several ancient peoples have explained this similarity by myths of a common origin for all humankind.

The Mesopotamians believed that the gods created the first humans out of clay from the earth, mixed with the blood and the flesh of a god. The deity's blood was the source of life and his flesh was the source of the soul. The Egyptians thought that humankind sprang from the tears of the gods. They considered human beings to be made of a common raw material, and hoped that they would join forces in the afterworld, where Egyptians, Syrians, Nubians and Libyans would co-operate to serve the sun god together.

In the biblical account, God created Adam from the dust of the earth, and Eve from Adam's rib. All the peoples and states known to the Israelites are represented as having sprung from a common ancestor, Noah, and before him, from Adam, the first man.

The Introductory Gallery presents humanity as a family. Noah's three sons — Shem, Ham and Japheth — were the ancestors of the three main divisions of humankind, as perceived by the Israelites.

The children of Shem were the ancestors of most of the Middle Eastern peoples - the Israelites, the Canaanites, the Assyrians, the Babylonians and the Syrians. The children of Ham were the Egyptians and the other peoples of Africa. The children of Japheth included the Greek and other Indo-European peoples of the Mediterranean, as far east as Asia Minor and the Caucasoid peoples of the Asian steppes. The Bactrians of Afghanistan, the Persians of Iran and the Urartians of Armenia, a powerful metal-working people contemporary with the Assyrians, were also the children of Japheth.

At the front of the entrance gallery you see three pedestal vitrines containing figures of men, women and children of these different ancient peoples, seen through their own eyes.

In one of the three pedestal vitrines is an elegant Greek *kouros* of bronze. He symbolises the perfection of mind and body that was the principal ideal of classical Greece, and is an example of the culture of the children of Japheth. The Semites (the children of Shem) are represented in the next pedestal vitrine by a Sabaean head (500-400 B.C.E.). The Sabaeans were an early people of Arabia. The fabled Queen of Sheba, who came to marvel at the wisdom of Solomon, probably came from this area. The third pedestal vitrine contains objects representing the children of Ham, including an Egyptian *ushabti* (a funerary statuette which was "activated" by spells and thought to work for the tomb owner

Fragment of a relief depicting Egyptian, Nubian and Syrian dignitaries; el-Amarna, Egypt, 1348-1335 B.C.E., BLMJ 1035

Door lintel of a synagogue; probably from the Golan, ca. 300-600 C.E., BLMJ 1105

Figure of a smiting god; Syria, ca. 1400 B.C.E., BLMJ 795

whenever required in the afterlife).

The relief fragment (1348-1335 B.C.E.) on the wall shows Nubian and Semitic visitors to the Egyptian royal court, accompanied by an Egyptian.

In the rear half of the entrance gallery, we have collected typical artefacts of the various peoples and periods of the ancient Near East. These objects are set in context with a relief map of the area, which shows the route of Abraham's journey from Ur to Canaan, and the major empires of antiquity. The key objects from each gallery shown here represent the different periods according to which the museum is arranged (the objects are labelled with the number of the gallery from which they come).

A hand-made clay bowl (1) from sixth millennium B.C.E. Anatolia represents the culture of the earliest settlements, when humans began to live in villages (ca. 8500 B.C.E.), became farmers and herders and started to make pottery (ca. 6000 B.C.E.). As human society grew more complex in the fifth millennium B.C.E. and people lived together in larger groups, various modes of symbolic communication overcame the limitations of time and space. The heart-shaped seal displayed here (3) may have been used to identify somebody's property by pressing it into a moist lump of clay which was used as a seal. The alabaster figure of a kneeling bull (2) from the fourth millennium B.C.E. represented divine power and fertility in the religion of Mesopotamia. The model ox-cart from Anatolia (from Gallery 5, ca. 2000 B.C.E.) shows the type of transport available to third- and second-millennia merchants as they carried their bundles of wares from city to city.

Terracotta figurines like this woman cuddling her baby (from Gallery 5, ca. 2750-1900 B.C.E.) have been found in many houses and buildings in Syria. They may represent a goddess or perhaps the donor herself. Apparently they conferred fertility, love, sex appeal and safe childbirth on the woman of the house.

The other figurine in this case (6) is a *lama* goddess from Mesopotamia (ca. 2200-1800 B.C.E.), a personal protector and patron, rather like a guardian angel. Such goddesses acted as intermediaries between their worshippers and the higher gods. Here she stands with her hands raised in prayer, wearing the divine horned crown. These statues were set up in the sanctuaries near the ear of the great god to transmit the requests of those who prayed to him in the temple. The texts tell us that they were made of gold and precious stones, which probably explains why so few of them remain. This more modest but rare copper alloy figure survived.

By the first half of the second millennium B.C.E., which according to certain scholars is the period of the Patriarchs, northern Syria was in the hands of the Amorites, makers of this rather mournful-looking blue faience face-shaped vase (9, ca. 1800-1600 B.C.E.). In Egypt, the elaborate mortuary cult which promised survival and happiness after death had existed for over a thousand years. It is represented here by the canopic jar (10, from 1550-1307 B.C.E.), which once contained some part of an ancient Egyptian's stomach, intestines, lungs or liver, mummified separately to avoid their putrefying in the stomach cavity. Similar jars might have been used for embalming Jacob and Joseph during the Israelites' sojourn in Egypt.

The gallery's survey of history and culture carries on in the second wall case, to the right.

The smiting god (10:1, ca. 1400 B.C.E.) was the weather god of the Syro-Canaanite pantheon, worshipped in Canaan before the arrival of the Israelites. His voice rang out in the thunder, and with the lightning he struck down his foes.

During the second half of the second millennium B.C.E., Akkadian was the "international language", much like English nowadays. Accounts, letters and legal texts were recorded in Akkadian on cuneiform tablets in the lands of the Hittites, Syrians and Babylonians. One of the two cuneiform tablets from Emar in Syria (10:2,3) records an interesting inheritance procedure whereby the daughters of the family were adopted as honorary "sons" by their stepfather so they could inherit the family's property.

Emar was part of the Hittite empire (ca.1400-1200 B.C.E.), represented by a silver stamp seal (10) from Anatolia, the Hittite heartland.

The period of migrations (ca. 1300-1100) which saw the end of the Hittite empire, the Exodus, major disruptions in Egypt and upheavals throughout the then-known world also witnessed the arrival of warlike nomadic tribes in the area of modern Iran. Their culture is represented here by a bronze plaque decorated with the face of a goddess (12).

After the Israelites settled in Canaan, they longed to be like other nations, and to have a king to organise them for defence against the attacks of their neighbours. After the rise of the monarchy, the division between rich and poor in Israelite society became much sharper. The ivory plaque of the cow suckling its calf (14:1, ca. 800 B.C.E.) hints at the luxurious objects, such as beds inlaid with ivory, owned by kings and nobles in the days of the kingdoms of Israel and Judah. The Assyrian cylinder seal (14:2) to the left, inscribed in Aramaic with the name of its owner Shallum, is also from this period.

Israel's position as a small country at the crossroads of the Fertile Crescent left her exposed to the ambitions of land-hungry empires. The objects in the last third of this survey represent the "super-powers" whose intervention in the area shaped Israel's history.

The small bronze figure (15, ca. 725-700 B.C.E.) is a deity of the Assyrians, who destroyed the kingdom of Israel on their way south in 722 B.C.E. Although Judah was heavily punished by the Assyrians, who sacked key cities such as Lachish, it was not entirely devastated.

The Assyrian empire was brought to an end in 609 B.C.E. by a coalition of Babylonian, Lydian and Median forces, and was followed by the rise of the Neo-Babylonian empire. In 586 B.C.E., a century and a half after the fall of the northern kingdom, the Babylonians conquered the kingdom of Judah and carried many of the Judaeans away in exile to Babylon. Their empire in turn was conquered in 539 B.C.E. by the Persian Cyrus, after he had overrun the Medes and Lydians. The splendid vase fragment (11) represents a Lydian of the mid-fifth century B.C.E., wearing huge earrings and with rouged cheeks. Fifth-century vase paintings show these long curls as characteristic of men rather than women, so this solemn and dramatic face is probably that of a young man.

A silver vessel (16:2) from Çesme in one of the pedestal vitrines and a golden earring (16:1) from the city of Sardis in Anatolia, the first or last station on the Persian Royal Road, represent the Persian empire, whose conquest of Babylon left the exiled Jews free to go home again. On their return to Israel, the exiles threw themselves into community rebuilding and religious revival, culminating in the reconstruction of the Temple. The flourishing society they developed was swallowed up in turn by both the Greek and the Roman empires. While under occupation by foreign powers, the Jews nonetheless struggled to retain their spiritual independence.

In the fourth century B.C.E., Alexander of Macedon conquered most of the known world, from Greece to India, and for a few years united it all in a single empire. The elaborate ring (17; its purpose is unknown) in the second pedestal vitrine is a product of Hellenistic culture, the Greek-based culture which flourished in the lands of the Middle East under Greek rule. The former Persian province of Yahud (Judaea) was caught up in the rivalries of Alexander's heirs as they scrambled for the remains of his empire. Initially part of the domain of the Ptolemies of Egypt, the province was eventually taken over by the Seleucid dynasty of Syria. The Seleucids tried to force Greek

Fragmentary vase in the shape of a head; Anatolia/ Lydia, ca. 450 B.C.E., BLMJ 164a,b

culture on their Jewish subjects against their will. The Books of the Maccabees record Jewish resistance to this arbitrary imposition of Greek culture.

Later, after a century and a half of independent nationhood under the rule of the Hasmonaeans, Judaea passed into the control of Herod the Great (37-4 B.C.E.) and then became a Roman province. Roman rule is represented by a bronze incense shovel, used in the official Roman cult of the gods.

The stone menorah displayed on the left as you leave this gallery once stood above the doorway of a synagogue in the Golan, built in the fourth to sixth centuries C.E. In the Temple of Solomon, the menorah of Moses was joined by ten new golden menoroth, which all disappeared in the destruction of the First Temple in 586 B.C.E. The Second Temple contained a single menorah, which is presumed to have been carried away by Titus when the Romans took Jerusalem and destroyed the Temple in 70 C.E. Its subsequent fate is unknown. A menorah, maybe the one from the Temple, is depicted on the Arch of Titus (see the wall panel in Gallery 18), carried in a triumphal procession. Today, the menorah, the age-old symbol of light, forms part of the emblem of the State of Israel.

GALLERY I

FROM HUNTER TO URBAN DWELLER

"Be fruitful and multiply, replenish the earth and have dominion over it... and over every living thing that moveth upon the earth."
(Genesis 1:28)

From 10,000 B.C.E. onwards, over a period of five thousand years, human beings revolutionised their relationship to the environment. Originally they lived as nomads, hunting wild animals and gathering wild plants and fruits. Gradually they began to settle down, developing a more settled lifestyle, moving between a summer and a winter site. Recent archaeological research suggests that this process of settling down preceded the domestication of animals and plants. People's new, more intensive and long-term relationship with the territory around these "proto-settlements" led to changes in the way they exploited the local plant and animal life. Little by little, they brought sheep, goats, pigs and cattle to depend on human caretakers. Gathering wild grains and fruits was gradually replaced by sowing, harvesting and storing wheat and barley. Humankind invented ploughs, sickles and mortars to replace the simple digging stick and their own bare hands.

Eventually they built permanent settlements and lived there all year round. This development took place over several thousand years, more quickly in some areas, more gradually in others. One of the far-reaching consequences of these

Bowl, painted and burnished baked clay; Anatolia, ca. 5400-5000 B.C.E., BLMJ 956

changes was that people lived in larger communities. A mobile group was limited to about 50 people, but the population of early villages reached 100-200.

You can see the earliest permanent settlements on the wall map, in the Levant and the foothills of western Iran and southern Anatolia, where rainfall was abundant, animals abounded and cereal crops grew wild. Once people had become more tied to their villages, they needed to increase the yield of the plants they ate by cultivating them.

Hacilar in southwestern Anatolia was a typical Neolithic village (see wall panel). In the early seventh millennium B.C.E., its inhabitants lived in small rectangular houses without doorways, which they entered by ladders. They grew barley and emmer wheat and probably kept animals, but did not yet make pottery. They may also have practised some form of ancestor worship, because plastered skulls were set up on the floors of certain buildings. Villages like Hacilar existed all over the area eastwards to the Tigris and southwards to the Negev.

A thousand years later in the early sixth millennium, Hacilar was still small. The houses had become more elaborate, with doorways, several rooms, stone foundations, mud-brick walls and a wooden upper storey. Each building probably housed a family of five to eight members, with an outdoor kitchen containing an oven, hearth, grinding stones and plastered bins for storing grain. Fewer hunting tools are found at this period; apparently, the people of Hacilar supported themselves mainly by agriculture. Pottery now becomes common; copper is known but still rare. The presence of spindle whorls shows that spinning and weaving were being developed, while finds of exotic items, such as seashells from the southern coast, show that long-distance trade was carried on. Terracotta female figurines are the only evidence we have of religion.

In about 5200 B.C.E., the village became more sophisticated. It was laid out with a central square and a thick mud-brick defensive wall.

This farming way of life grew so successful that by about 5500 B.C.E., people were able to leave the fertile foothills and settle in less hospitable areas. By the end of the fifth millennium B.C.E., all regions of the Near East were occupied. The presence of a few towns hinted at the changes which were to come.

Flaked stone tools (like those in the first pedestal vitrine) are among the earliest traces of human activity. Before and after the invention of metal-working, people used flaked stone blades to reap grain, scrape hides and chop wood.

Later, other useful or beautiful objects were made of ground stone, such as bowls and palettes for grinding eye-paint. You can see some examples in the second pedestal vitrine.

Clay was originally used as a supplementary material — to line grain bins to keep rats and mice out, to waterproof houses, and to line baskets. During the eighth to seventh millennia B.C.E., people discovered how to fire clay to make pottery. By experimenting, they found out many different ways to decorate their vessels — they incised or painted designs on their pots, painted them with a slip of clay mixed with water, or burnished them after firing to make their surface more attractive. Look out for early examples of the potter's art from Hacilar in the third pedestal vitrine. Note the different types of decoration: painting, burnishing or polishing, and incising.

Somebody who wove textiles may have thought up the idea of a stamp like this one next to the pots in order to print a design on the fabric — a labour-saving device from 6000 B.C.E. Later, when pots were used to store oil, wine or food, stamp seals of this type were used on the lid fastening to show ownership.

Even at this period, people imported raw materials not available locally, such as obsidian, which they exchanged for crops, animals, local raw materials or objects they had made themselves. This trade passed from village to village, rather than via merchants.

The fourth pedestal vitrine contains objects from northern Mesopotamia. The first evidence for the use of seals for administrative purposes comes from the Halaf culture. The two stamp seals shown here are typical examples.

From these simple beginnings, more complex societies developed during the fourth millennium B.C.E. (the Uruk period). Earlier, society had been organized along kinship lines: individuals lived in small villages and owed allegiance to their family, tribe or clan. Now, with the development of cities, people were grouped together on the basis of a common citizenship, with both men and women carrying out functions in society irrespective of blood ties.

The first full-time professional craftsmen appeared, stimulating the growth of long-distance trade. Uruk (biblical Erech) was the first great trade emporium in the world. Its merchants set up trading colonies all over Anatolia, Syria, Mesopotamia and Iran — small communities of merchants with their own cylinder seals and expatriate Mesopotamian culture. This trade, in turn, brought in wealth to the new cities. Cities gradually grew in size and complexity: the city of Uruk occupied 100 hectares in the Late Uruk period (ca. 3300 B.C.E.), and grew to 400 hectares, surrounded by a city wall, by the Early Dynastic I period (ca. 2900 B.C.E.).

New tools such as the potter's wheel and the mould made it possible to mass-produce vessels for expanding markets. On the other side of the case featuring artefacts from southern Mesopotamia (between Galleries 1 and 4) are three cylinder seals showing pigtailed men and women with vessels. These seals were used by the largely female institutions which produced manufactured goods by spinning, weaving and pottery-making — all shown on the seals of this group. Inlaid bowls were also made for the first time during this period (3500-2900 B.C.E.).

Modest temples such as the shrine of Hacilar were replaced by mighty monuments such as the temple precinct of Eanna in the sacred city of Uruk. On the gallery wall by the entrance to Gallery 2, we have rendered a typical niched temple façade, like those depicted on the cylinder seals.

This Mesopotamian design looks surprisingly similar to the façade of an Egyptian mastaba. The use of niched façades and cylinder seals in Egypt, as well as the idea of writing, indicate indirect links between Mesopotamia and Egypt in the late fourth millennium.

Seals in the wall box on the "temple façade" may have belonged to the temple administration, or ordinary people may have wanted to set a picture of the holy place on their seals in order to obtain the gods' blessing. The temple was not only a spiritual centre but operated workshops, sponsored technological development and provided work.

In Egypt, during the second half of the fourth millennium B.C.E., two contrasting societies developed in the different halves of the country. In the north, small trading centres sprang up, with commercial links as far afield as Lebanon, Syria and Mesopotamia. In the south, an elitist culture developed, oriented towards display and ceremony. Towards 3100 B.C.E., the south gradually conquered the north, and Egypt was eventually united under a single ruler.

The stone maceheads in the next case may have seen service in the wars of conquest, although maceheads were also made for ceremonial use. The mace was the first weapon designed especially to kill human beings.

The new monarchy and its courtiers desired prestige. They promoted the development of the hieroglyphic script and the elaborate mortuary cult. The elegant stone vessels exhibited here (3110-2870 B.C.E.) may have come from wealthy people's tombs, where they would have held food, wine, beer or ointment for use in the afterlife.

Female figurine of baked and painted clay; Halaf culture, Mesopotamia or Syria, ca. 5300-4500 B.C.E., BLMJ 814

GALLERY 2

THE ANNE & JOSEPH TERNBACH GALLERY

THE COMING OF CIVILISATION

As men migrated from the east they found a plain in the land of Shinar and settled there. And they said to one another, "Come, let us make bricks and burn them thoroughly... Come, let us build ourselves a city, and a tower with its top in the sky..."
(Genesis 11: 2-4)

The focal points of the Mesopotamian cities of the late fourth millennium were the temples, "the houses of heaven". These ritual and spiritual centres were also economic institutions containing workshops and storerooms. The temples owned flocks and land and fostered craftsmanship. Craftsmen would receive raw materials from the temples, and would be paid for the finished product — a sort of piece-work system. Tithes and offerings formed an important part of the temples' income, and were redistributed to the public as rations and salaries for temple staff, payment for stone, luxury goods and other materials and wages for the services of craftsmen. The temples dominated the city architecturally as well as economically — on the skyline, the city dweller would see the massive temple buildings, the residence of the god.

In the city, most people specialized in a particular type of work. They might be full-time craftsmen, priests or priestesses, merchants, civil servants or military officials. Lists of titles and professions, written to serve as reference texts, began to appear in Mesopotamia in about 3100 B.C.E. They record the existence of smiths, seal-cutters, leather-workers, doctors, diviners, teachers, millers, entertainers and many other specialists. In the neolithic village, on the other hand, people turned their hands to every available task— sowing and reaping, taking their animals to pasture, and repairing their houses according to the season.

Lion-shaped amulet; Mesopotamia, Sumer, ca. 3300-2900 B.C.E., BLMJ 2908

There had already been some craft specialisation — we know of a potters' quarter in one village in about 5800 B.C.E.— but with the shift to the city, this specialisation became far more pronounced as the craftsmen began to produce large quantities of goods for a mass market. These craftsmen used more sophisticated technical equipment than their predecessors, such as the potter's wheel, metal-worker's mould and the stonecutter's drill.

People living in the neolithic villages had to produce their own food in order to survive. Fourth-millennium city dwellers, however, often exchanged a specialised type of labour for somebody else's agricultural produce.

The surplus crops which made craft specialisation possible also made it feasible for people to trade, both locally and over long distances, to obtain other commodities they needed or desired. Trade began during the neolithic period, when the Anatolian villages imported obsidian from hundreds of miles away, but by the mid-fourth millennium this trickle of commerce had become a river. Trade was vital for Mesopotamia, where the only local resource was mud, and by the mid- to late fourth millennium a chain of Uruk merchant colonies had sprung up in an arc stretching from the Euphrates through northern Syria and Anatolia away into Assyria and Iran. They imported stone and timber for building, and metals for weapons and tools.

In order for people who had never met each other to communicate at a distance, writing evolved.

The need to keep written records of sales and tithes gave impetus to writing. Most literate Mesopotamians acquired their education with the aim of working in trade or administration.

City life provided a stimulus to intellectual creativity. Beyond subsistence, the leisure to think and ponder and the presence of other inquiring minds inspired learned scribes to create systems of science and philosophy, and priests to evolve complex ritual systems.

However, most of these changes only touched a minority of people directly. Only a small percentage of the population lived in towns. The others, the farmers and peasants, were directly affected mostly by canal maintenance, temple tithes and compulsory labour on public projects, such as temple-building.

Some of the beliefs and wishes dear to the people of Mesopotamia in the fourth millennium B.C.E. appear on the seals and amulets displayed in this gallery.

Seal impression showing a man in prayer before a reed gatepost, symbol of the goddess Inanna; Mesopotamia, Jemdet Nasr culture, ca. 3100-2900 B.C.E., BLMJ 2607

Impression of a cylinder seal showing a bull and a stalk of corn; Mesopotamia, Uruk period, ca. 3300-3100 B.C.E., BLMJ 2528

About ninety per cent of the society still lived directly off the land, by farming and herding. They knew they were vulnerable to famine, drought and disease, and thus they showed special reverence to the powers which could save them from hunger. The cylinder seal (3, in the wall box) showing a bull with an ear of corn (ca. 3300-3100 B.C.E.) represents its owner's hopes for an increase of crops and herds.

Bulls figure again on the limestone and copper bowls in the pedestal vitrine (3300-3100 B.C.E.). Their controlled might symbolised the power of the divine. Look carefully at the stone bowl supported by the two bulls and you will see that the carver has succeeded in expressing the different textures of the bulls' bodies in stone — their soft noses, fleshy facial skin and bony foreheads. One bull seems a little older than its companion. Its head is more massive, and deep folds of skin stretch from its neck to the inner corner of its eyes. The second bull is plumper and has more tautly drawn skin.

The Mesopotamians experienced divine power as dwelling in some specific feature of the visible, physical, earthly world, causing it to be and live and flourish. In contrast, the ancient Hebrews understood divine power as transcendent. In the account of Moses' meeting with God in the burning bush in Exodus, chapter 3, it is quite clear that God is totally distinct from the bush out of which He chose to speak to Moses. Ancient Mesopotamians would have experienced such a confrontation differently. They would have heard and seen the numinous power, but as the power of the bush itself, not just in the bush.

The goddess Inanna personified the divine power of the (temple) storehouse, replete with fertility and plenty. Her heraldic symbol, the reed gatepost, appears on a green calcite cylinder seal (1, in the wallbox).

On the Uruk vase depicted on the large wall panel, first fruits are offered to the goddess Inanna. At the bottom of the vase the earth brings forth its fruit and the flocks increase and multiply. Again, the blessing of fertility is expressed by the combination of cattle and grain. In the middle, naked priests in procession bring baskets of food and vessels of drink. At the top of the vase, Inanna herself, wearing the horned headdress that symbolised divinity, presides over the sanctuary while her high priest and the ruler present the first fruits of their produce to her on behalf of her people.

In the second pedestal vitrine are

typical Mesopotamian amulets and seals from the period 3300-2900 B.C.E. Seals were used to mark objects (see also Gallery 3), whereas amulets protected their wearer from evil and from harm. They depict bulls, cows, rams, monkeys, birds, vultures, lions, wild boars, turtles — and even a hedgehog.

Vessel supported by recumbent bulls, BLMJ 860; bowl carved with bulls in relief, BLMJ 818; Mesopotamia, Uruk period, ca. 3300-3100 B.C.E.

GALLERY 3

THE ANA & ABRAHAM PORTNOY GALLERY

SYMBOLIC COMMUNICATION

And he said: "What pledge shall I give thee?" And she said: "Thy seal and thy cord and thy staff that is in thy hand."
(Genesis 38:18)

Before writing was invented, people transmitted knowledge from one generation to the next by word of mouth. When they needed to jog their memories, they sometimes used symbols to represent some object or event.

As trade brought the need to send messages over great distances, people began to communicate by symbols in a more sophisticated way. They communicated by making deliberate marks with a seal on a given surface, leaving an impression which could be understood by other people. Seal impressions identified their owner then, just as signatures do nowadays. Seal impressions on lumps of clay served to protect the contents of jars, boxes and baskets, and goods in storerooms behind closed doors, preventing unauthorized persons from gaining access to the objects under seal by showing whether someone had tampered with the container or door.

The earliest seals, used from the sixth to fifth millennia B.C.E., were stamp seals. Made of clay or stone, they have raised, pierced backs and bases carved with a design.

Seals not only identified but also guarded the property they marked. As

Side (left) and face (right) of a Neo-Babylonian stamp seal with an Aramaic inscription; Mesopotamia, ca. 625-539 B.C.E., BLMJ seal 1062e

such, they were considered a type of amulet, and often their back was carved in the shape of an animal to bless and protect the seal's owner. For example, the amulet shaped like a lion's head from early third millennium Mesopotamia (ca. 3100-2900 B.C.E.) may have been thought to make its owner fearless.

Certain materials from which seals were made were also held to bring good fortune. Banded agate conferred riches and a good name, green marble would bring favours, and lapis lazuli would confer dignity and divine favour on its owner. Many of these stones were imported from distant countries — lapis lazuli, for example, came from distant Afghanistan. Because of their splendour and rarity such seals were often worn as jewellery, status symbols of their owner's wealth.

Carving such seals, of course, was a specialised craft which took years to master. We know the names of seal-cutters from the third millennium, but little is known about the learning process until contracts appear during the first millennium. In these texts, the apprentice promises to stay with the master-craftsman for four years, during which he will learn to carve and identify all the stones.

At some time during the fourth millennium, the cylinder seal was invented. This is a stone cylinder, with a hole for suspension bored through it lengthwise. The design incised on the surface of the seal stands out as a continuous band of raised relief when the cylinder is rolled over a moist clay surface.

In the third millennium the owner's name, or his name and title, was added to the design. As time went on, this information became more and more elaborate and some second millennium seals even include dedications, prayers and incantations.

Seals could be used as a mark of ownership, or of responsibility for the objects under seal. Clerks and officials were in charge of the seal of their superior, or of an institution, like the modern rubber stamp. Cylinder seals were much more suitable than the earlier stamp seals for this type of sealing because they protected a much wider surface. If anyone tampered with the sealing, it was far more difficult to hide the traces of their meddling.

People who owned seals came from all strata of society — aristocrats and commoners, kings, peasants and slaves. Every individual, whether male or female, had legal rights and judicial standing. Three of the seals shown here belonged to Enikattim the fuller, Arad-mu the chair bearer, and Ur-Lama the worker who plaited reeds around clay vessels.

Cylinder seals were worn as part of a string of beads, or on pins which secured garments; some texts even record that these pins, with seals attached, were used as murder weapons! Seals were also set into rings.

In Egypt, cylinder seals were popular during the first two dynasties. At the end of the Old Kingdom, however, they were replaced by stamp seals, often worn as rings. From about 2200 B.C.E., the back of the seal was often carved in the form of a scarab beetle. The scarab was associated with the sun's journey across heaven, one's wishes coming true, and the resurrection of the soul. Like the scarab beetle rolling a ball of dung as its food supply, the sun god was thought to emerge in scarab form from his night journey through the underworld and propel the sun across the morning sky.

Towards the end of the first millennium B.C.E., the ornamental role of seals began to be as important as their practical use. They were made of gems, the hardest stones available, and set in rings of gold and silver to enhance their splendour.

An interactive display computer programme, installed in this gallery, allows you to obtain information about 120 different seals on display in this gallery, or elsewhere in the museum. With any seal as your starting point, you can trace your own individual route of discovery

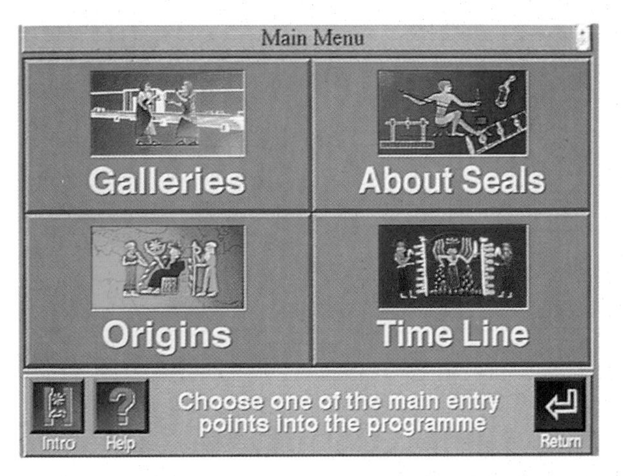

Four main menu buttons are your entry points into the program.

The historical context, geographical origin and symbolic analysis of each seal, accompanied by a soundtrack, can be investigated.

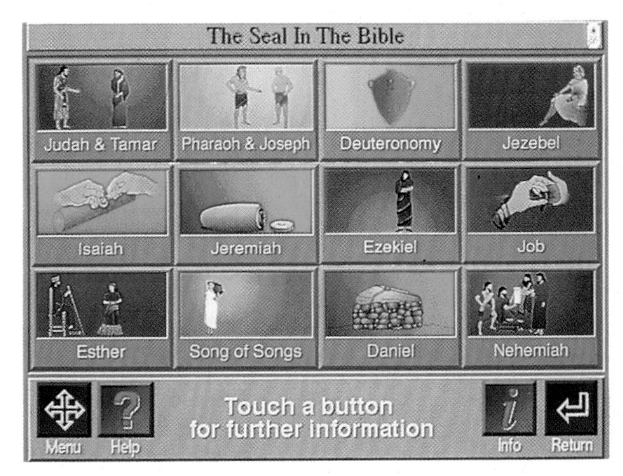

Access to a wealth of additional information is gained via the background button. Shown above are buttons you can press to find out about seals and sealing in the Bible.

through an almost infinite network of cross-references, never returning to the same point twice. You can view impressions of your chosen seal, use a glossary with more than a hundred entries to learn more about the area where the seal was found and the ancient names and titles featured on the seal, and see the seal in context plotted on maps and time-lines. Choosing another starting point, you can wander across the map of the ancient Near East, picking up seals which are associated with each area, or select a period from the time-line and view seals from that era. You can also learn more about how seals were made and used, who owned them, and different types of seals.

The computer's touch screen puts all this information at your fingertips. It is not difficult to use; even people who "hate computers" can feel at ease with it. The display is enhanced by a sound-track, artwork and colour photographs.

Impression of a cylinder seal depicting a king standing victorious between two animals. Aramaic inscription "Seal of Smsk*"; Persia, ca. 538-332 B.C.E., BLMJ seal 499*

GALLERY 4

LITERATE VOICES:

THE BEGINNING OF WRITING

And it came to pass, when Moses made an end of writing the words of this Torah in a book until they were finished, that Moses commanded the Levites that bore the ark of the covenant of the Lord, saying: "Take this book of the Torah and put it by the side of the ark of the covenant of the Lord your God, that it may be there for a witness against thee".
(Deuteronomy 31:24-26)

Not only the Israelites but all the peoples of the ancient Near East were "Peoples of the Book". Their lives and views of the world were shaped by the written word. Although their cultures and civilisations disappeared long ago, their monuments and inscriptions have survived for us to decipher.

The keys to the decipherment of these ancient languages were multilingual texts, such as the inscription on the alabaster vessel displayed in the pedestal vitrine at the beginning of the gallery. The inscription contains a date — the 36th regnal year of the Persian king Darius I (486 B.C.E.). It is written in four of the languages and three of the scripts used in the huge Persian empire: Old Persian (Indo-European, written in alphabetic cuneiform), Akkadian (Semitic, written in syllabic cuneiform), Elamite (a language unrelated to any linguistic family, written in syllabic cuneiform) and Egyptian (Hamito-Semitic, written in Egyptian hieroglyphs). Look out for traces of colour, left by the famous Phoenician purple dye made from the murex shell.

How did this babel of scripts come into being? As trade grew, merchants thousands of miles away from each other needed to communicate more reliably than by sending a spoken message via middlemen or by using the limited symbolic system discussed in Gallery 3. They would seal small tokens representing their goods into balls of clay, which could be broken on arrival to check that nothing had been lost or stolen. In time, these tokens were replaced by pictures on a flat surface, and then by representative marks. This process took place in southern Mesopotamia in the late fourth millennium B.C.E., and provided the stimulus for the invention of writing.

In the first wall niche, to your left, are texts written in cuneiform, the script invented in Mesopotamia. Cuneiform was used to write many different languages — Sumerian, Akkadian (Assyrian and Babylonian), Hurrian, Urartian, Hittite and Elamite, representing five different language families over three millennia.

Cuneiform began as a pictographic script, and developed into a stylised form which could be written on a raw material which the Mesopotamians had in plenty — mud. Cuneiform was written by pressing the end of the stylus into a tablet of damp clay, to make wedge-shaped marks in various arrangements. Hence modern European scholars call this script cuneiform, "wedge-shaped writing", from the Latin word "cuneus", wedge. Once the clay dried, the tablet was hard. Sometimes tablets were baked in an oven, which made them more durable. Cuneiform script could also be incised on stone objects of varying sizes — from large inscriptions (2, 12) to tiny cylinder

Alabaster vessel bearing royal inscription of Darius I, in four languages (detail, hieroglyphic inscription); Egypt, 486 B.C.E., BLMJ 1979

seals (e.g. 5, 8).

All sorts of subjects were recorded in cuneiform texts: for example, literary texts, administrative records (1), royal inscriptions (4), poetry, dedications (7), contracts and inventories (3,6) and scientific texts.

In the next wall niche, dedicated by Mrs. Ayala Deutsch in memory of her late husband Prof. Menachem (Victor) Deutsch, are examples of the hieroglyphic script. Like cuneiform, it began its career as a pictographic script. Although the signs are clearly identifiable pictures, it is not a purely ideographic system, where each sign represents a separate word. Some signs were used to write individual words, others represented a sound, or combinations of two or three sounds, and still others were written at the ends of words to clarify the meanings of those words (determinatives). Look at the extreme left edge of the brightly painted fragment (2, dated to 1550-1307 B.C.E.) and you will see a tiny part of a picture of a ship, written at the end of the word "sailing".

Hieroglyphs were mostly used for monumental inscriptions, such as the doorpost with Ramesses III's cartouches (4, dated to 1194-1163 B.C.E.), the blue faience plaque with Ramesses II's cartouche (3), part of a foundation deposit from one of the temples he built, and the lintel (1) from an Old Kingdom tomb with its owner's titles (2486-2440 B.C.E.). The last four signs to the left write his name, Ka-aper, using a combination of word-

Fragment of a Neo-Hittite hieroglyphic stele; Anatolia, ca. 1000-700 B.C.E., BLMJ 1104

Administrative tablet; Mesopotamia, Jemdet Nasr culture, ca. 3000 B.C.E., BLMJ 1145

signs and sound-signs.

Everyday texts such as letters, accounts and legal documents were written in hieratic, a cursive script derived from hieroglyphs (see the wall panel to the left of the niche). Early hieratic is very similar to hieroglyphs, but its later forms have already taken on a life of their own. If you look at the hieratic papyrus in the wall box at the end of the gallery you will probably not recognise most of the signs.

By the seventh century B.C.E., this script had become so abbreviated that it bore little relation to its hieroglyphic prototype. This very cursive script is known as demotic. By then, the earlier forms of hieratic had fallen out of everyday use but were still used for writing religious texts, such as the page from the Book of the Dead in the wall box (664-525 B.C.E.), which provided the correct answers to satisfy the dreaded doorkeepers of the afterworld and ensured that its owner would enter the realm of the dead safely.

Hieratic and demotic were written with a reed pen and ink on papyri, potsherds and pieces of stone. The scribe did not rest his hand on the papyrus as he wrote, but painted the signs, rather like a Chinese calligrapher.

Besides cuneiform, the Hittites used another script, the "Hittite" (more correctly, Luvian) hieroglyphic script, which was a local Anatolian invention. This script was used in monumental inscriptions of the mid-second to early first millennia B.C.E. Many of the signs on the black basalt fragment (8) are easily recognisable, such as the human head. Like the Egyptian script, the Hittite signs represented words or combinations of sounds (syllables in this case; the Hittites wrote vowels, unlike the Egyptians).

In the last wall niche are examples of the alphabetic scripts. The (Proto)-Canaanite script of the early second millennium was developed further by the Phoenicians, and later by the Israelites, who learnt it from the Canaanites when they settled in Canaan (see the wall panel to the left of this niche). The English word "alphabet" is based on *alpha* and *beta*,

Jar handle stamped with impression of private stamp seal: "Belonging to Menahem, the son of Yobnah" (below, detail); Israel, 700-600 B.C.E., BLMJ 863

Lapis lazuli seal bearing Phoenician inscription: "Belonging to the governor of Rimon"; Levant, ca. 700-600 B.C.E., BLMJ 156

the first two letters of the Greek alphabet, derived from the Semitic letters *aleph* and *beth*.

The Canaanite script is exemplified here by the arrowhead (1) in the centre of the case, which belonged to a man named Shmida, who lived during the days of the Judges, in about 1050 B.C.E. The blue lapis lazuli seal of the governor of Rimon (ca. 800-600 B.C.E.) is engraved with Phoenician script (2). The jar handle (4) and ostracon (3) on the left are inscribed with early Hebrew letters (800-600 B.C.E.). The Phoenician script developed into Punic. The Punic stela from Carthage (12) at the rear of the case commemorates a dedication or sacrifice made to the goddess Taanit and the god Baal-Hammon in fulfilment of a vow (300-200 B.C.E.).

The Canaanite script also gave rise to archaic Greek (the ancestor of Greek and Latin scripts), represented by the small statuette base (510-490 B.C.E.) with a dedicatory inscription to the god Apollo in archaic Greek script (7).

The Aramaic script (9) was another offshoot of the Canaanite script, as are all the alphabetic scripts in use today — including modern Hebrew, Arabic, Iranian (Pahlavi) and Hindi, besides Greek and Latin. Two other scripts descended from Aramaic were the pre-Manichaean script and the Babylonian Jewish Aramaic script. The two bowls on the right, one written in pre-Manichaean (10), one in Jewish Aramaic (11), are demon traps from the cities of Babylonia at the time of the Talmud and the Gaonim (500-600 C.E.). They were placed upside down in the

Sabaean stela with royal building inscription; Arabia, Marib, ca. 400 B.C.E., BLMJ 3008

Calcite bowl bearing cuneiform inscription of Sharkalisharri, king of Akkade; Mesopotamia, Akkad, ca. 2189-2164 B.C.E., BLMJ 920

foundations of a house to protect its inhabitants from evil spirits.

On the rear wall of the gallery is an example of Palmyran Aramaic, inscribed on a stone stele. On the other side of the wall box with the example of Egyptian hieratic script (which also contains a pair of gilded slippers that belonged to a Coptic bishop, decorated with the words "Be healthy!") is a marble slab inscribed in the classical Latin script used by the Romans — that is the direct ancestor of today's Latin script, used to write a huge variety of languages.

In the nearby pedestal vitrine are coins inscribed in another Aramaic script, Nabataean, the forerunner of the classical Arabic script.

In the central vitrine, you can see examples of a different branch of the Proto-Canaanite family of alphabets, the Arabian scripts used by the Arabian kingdoms of the first millennium B.C.E. Thamudic script was used in the north and Sabaean in the south. These are the ancestors of the modern Ethiopic alphabet, which is used for writing the Ethiopian languages, such as Ge'ez (the classical language of Ethiopia, which is used by both Christians and Jews for writing their sacred scriptures), Amharic and Tigre.

GALLERY 5

THE PRE-PATRIARCHAL WORLD

And Jacob rose up... and the sons of Israel carried Jacob, their father, and their little ones, and their wives, in the wagons which Pharaoh sent to carry him.
(Genesis 46:5)

The Fertile Crescent of the third millennium was home to several sophisticated societies, knitted together by international trade. Caravan routes and shipping linked distant cities, the rich enjoyed imported luxuries, and an elaborate mythology gave meaning to people's lives. This is the setting of the earliest chapters of Genesis.

This gallery concentrates on contemporary religious life and commerce.

In the first pedestal vitrine as you enter the gallery, you will see two lively bulls made of bronze and an openwork bronze disc ornamented with stags' heads. These pieces once formed part of "standards", which may have been used in religious rituals. Similar examples have been found in the "royal" tombs at Alaca Hüyük, in northern central Anatolia, which were probably the graves of semi-nomadic chieftains. Their elaborate and beautifully finished design demonstrates the technical mastery of the metal-workers at this period. One of the two bulls (3) bears an inlaid plaque on its forehead, made of electrum — an alloy of gold and silver.

In the first case in this gallery are pillar-shaped clay statuettes from Syria and violin-shaped figures from Anatolia.

The Syrian statuettes (2750-1900 B.C.E.) depict women wearing elaborate jewellery and headdresses. They were buried under houses in northeastern Syria, and probably represent their owner's hopes for fertility — many children, safe childbirth and a wonderful love life. However, we cannot be certain of this, because no texts accompany them. The figures might be guardian goddesses who interceded for their worshippers before the chief gods. The figurines with holes in their arms may have held divine insignia, such as the axe and mace of the thunder god, or maybe gripped chariot reins. Some scholars even suggest that these figurines were dolls.

The Anatolian figurines (2900-2000 B.C.E.), made of baked clay or stone, were found in tombs. Look closely at them and you will see that they have been mended. They were found with their heads broken off — ritually "killed", perhaps to banish the dead person's ghost.

In the next case, bronze and baked clay models of ox-carts show how people of the Fertile Crescent travelled during the third millennium. In these huge, heavy wagons with their giant wheels, merchants drove thousands of miles between the trading centres of the ancient Near East. Abram may have transported his household and belongings in a cart of this type, when he left Ur to come to Canaan.

A seal (7) in this case shows a ship with a high prow and stern, probably built of reed bundles lashed together. Such ships were used for sea and river trade.

Despite these clumsy methods of transport, long-distance trade was common throughout the Fertile Crescent.

During the third millennium B.C.E., Mesopotamia was the centre of a gigantic trade network, stretching west to Anatolia and east to India. Mesopotamia had no

"Pillar figurines"; Syria or Mesopotamia, ca. 2750-1900 B.C.E., BLMJ 585, 595

metal resources and most raw materials had to be imported. The three main trading points to the east were Dilmun (Bahrain), Magan (probably both sides of the Gulf of Oman) and Meluḫḫa (the Indus valley). Trade with these areas was so lucrative that Meluḫḫa established its own colonies and depots in the city of Ur, from which merchants set out along the long road home by sea and land. Trade goods travelled west to Babylonia; in the early second millennium, the Assyrians brought them westwards. They exported the celebrated Babylonian textiles and tin from Afghanistan to Anatolia and imported silver and probably gold.

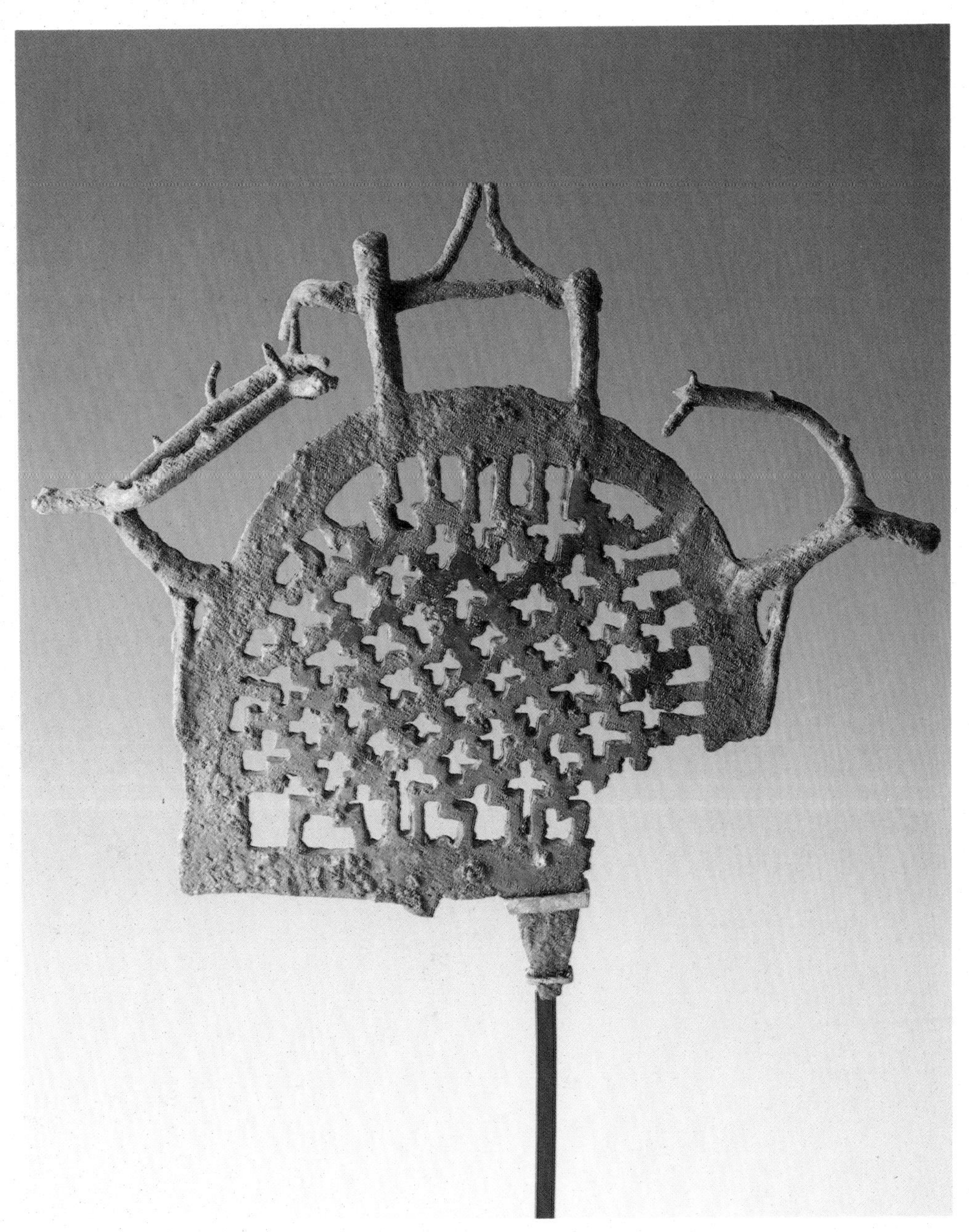

Finial from a standard; Anatolia, ca. 2500-2000 B.C.E., BLMJ 392, Gift of Leon Pomerantz

Inscribed calcite bowl; Mesopotamia, Akkad, ca. 2246-2190 B.C.E., BLMJ 929

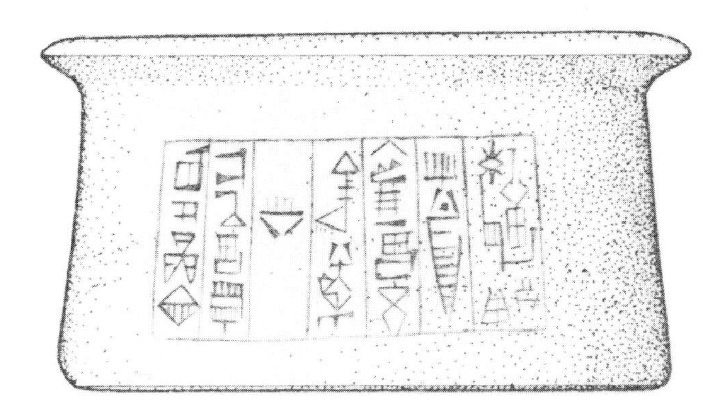

Drawing of the above bowl showing the inscription:
"Naram-Sin, king of the four quarters, a vase [from] the booty of Magan".

Well-to-do Mesopotamians lived luxuriously, delighting in fine clothes and jewellery. On a small shell inlay plaque (2500-2370 B.C.E.), displayed in the next case to the left, you can see an elegant lady sniffing a flower at a banquet (4). She would probably have worn bracelets (1-2), gold earrings (13-14), rings (8), hair

Ruler's head from Mari; Syria, ca. 2600-2350 B.C.E., BLMJ 159, anonymous gift

Wagon drawn by bulls; Anatolia, ca. 2000 B.C.E., BLMJ 260

clasps (12) and a gold and lapis lazuli necklace (10-11) like those in the case. Before the party, she would anoint herself with perfumed oils from alabaster vessels, like the container with two rams' heads (5). She would make up her face using an applicator, like the one with the wicked-looking demon's face (6).

In the nearby pedestal vitrine is a hoard of Sumerian treasure from about 2500 B.C.E., discovered in Syria. It includes pendants, beads, necklaces and ear plugs (8) in rare and expensive materials — carnelian, lapis lazuli, mother of pearl, rock crystal, gold and silver.

The last case shows the "office equipment" of the local traders and foreign merchants. Here are seals from Bactria (5-8) and from Anatolia, where the Assyrians had a trading colony at Kültepe during the early second millennium B.C.E. Note the clay tablet (1) on which the merchant Shesh-Kalla wrote his accounts in approximately 2043 B.C.E. Another tablet (10), with accounts of the overland trade to Anatolia, is still wrapped in its protective envelope (1920-1850 B.C.E.). The third and largest tablet displayed (2) lists some of the materials — gold, silver, copper and tin — sought in western Iran by the Sumerians, in this case by means of a raid rather than by more peaceful commercial means. Two beautifully decorated examples of the small soft stone vessels imported from southern Iran via the Persian Gulf are also shown here (3-4).

Certain key points along the trade routes flourished as commercial centers, such as Mari and Ebla.

In the pedestal vitrine near the wall panels, in the corner of the gallery, is a cuneiform tablet with administrative records from the royal palace of Ebla (modern Tell Mardikh near Aleppo). Ebla stood at the crossroads of the Syrian trade routes, midway between the Euphrates and the Mediterranean. It handled huge amounts of trade and was fabulously wealthy (see wall panel).

In the 1970s, the city was excavated. The finds included exotic raw materials, such as lapis lazuli, and many other items of interest, but overshadowing everything else was the discovery of a greater

Shell inlay showing a woman; Mesopotamia, Sumer, ca. 2500-2370 B.C.E., BLMJ 2026

treasure — the huge archive containing thousands of documents of every type: religious texts, accounts, legal texts, historical records and letters. This new information is changing some of the most basic ideas which scholars previously held about life in Syria and Mesopotamia in the third millennium B.C.E. This particular tablet (ca. 2400 B.C.E.) lists shipments of barley from the palace to various destinations. The circles and semi-circles represent amounts of barley. Some of the consignments were sent to nearby villages as seed for planting and rations, others were traded with distant cities such as Mari, 400 kilometres away.

Mari was the westernmost outpost of Sumerian culture, a bustling metropolis with palaces and temples galore, whose rulers appear as one of the early dynasties of Sumer (see the wall panel).

The tablet in the next pedestal vitrine, displayed with two statue fragments, mentions an exchange carried out in Mari in about 2400 B.C.E., with barley being bartered for fish.

The tiny pinkish calcite bowl in the gallery's central pedestal vitrine comes from Magan on the Persian Gulf, a polity on both shores of the Gulf of Oman. This vessel was taken as booty by King Naram-Sin of Akkad (ca. 2246-2190 B.C.E.) and inscribed with a short dedicatory inscription before being deposited in a temple. His inscriptions claim that he brought back vast amounts of booty from Magan, but little of it has been preserved. "Booty bowls" like this were probably dedicated to a god or used as containers for ceremonial food offerings, or as memorial pieces which the king gave his warriors in honour of the victory. A hundred and forty years ago, a bowl with an inscription identical to this one was discovered by the French in Babylon. The scholar Sir Henry Rawlinson copied its inscription. It was then lost for a century in a shipwreck on the Tigris. Our bowl may be the same one, though it is impossible to prove this.

Baked clay chariot with two figures; Syria, ca. 2100-1650 B.C.E., BLMJ 949

The other object in this vitrine is another example of a piece of booty taken by the Old Akkadian kings, who founded an empire that stretched from Iran to Anatolia. The lapis lazuli of which it is made was imported from the eastern hinterland of Iran, and was probably carved into a medallion in Lagash, where it would have adorned a royal or divine statue in the Early Dynastic III period (ca. 2500 B.C.E.). Later, between 2272 and 2263 B.C.E., the second king of the Akkadian dynasty invaded Lagash, carried off the medallion with the rest of his booty, and inscribed it with his name — Rimush king of Kish.

GALLERY 6

THE ZEEV REUBEN BOROWSKI GALLERY

THE SUMERIAN TEMPLE

Praise ye the Lord, Praise God in His sanctuary... Praise him upon the loud cymbals, Praise him upon the high sounding cymbals
(Psalm 150:1,5)

This gallery presents a panorama of Sumerian religion during the third millennium B.C.E.: its gods and goddesses, deified kings, temples, the human and animal forms it used to portray divine forces, and some of its rituals.

The gallery itself has been designed in the form of a Sumerian sanctuary — a "holy of holies". The focal point of the shrine would have been the deity's statue, which would have stood in the wall niche at the end, where we have displayed the horned diadem.

The case to the right as you enter the gallery shows the gods of Sumer themselves, depicted on seals from the late third millennium B.C.E.

The religious metaphors of the early third millennium portrayed human life as endangered by war and raiding bandits as much as by famine. These metaphors now included concepts of rulership, as people relied on the gods to protect them from their enemies.

Each god or goddess was the patron of a given city, and together they sat in the democratic assembly of the gods in the holy city of Nippur, presided over by Enlil the great ruler-god and god of the air, son of An, chief of all gods. Enlil's son was the great moon-god Nanna/Sin, and Nanna/Sin's children were the gods of the cosmos, Utu/Shamash the sun, god of justice, Inanna/Ishtar the planet Venus, goddess of love and war, and the storm god Ishkur/Adad.

During the third millennium, the Sumerians and the Akkadians lived side by side. The Sumerian pantheon was reorganised and Sumerian deities were amalgamated with Akkadian ones. As a result, most of the Mesopotamian deities were known by a Sumerian name (the first of the pair) but they were also given names in Akkadian.

The highest Sumerian gods recognized in all Sumer were An, Enlil, Ninhursag, the "Lady of the Mountain," the "Nourisher" and wet-nurse of kings and Enki/Ea. Ninhursag is commemorated here on the personal seal (2) of a wet-nurse named Daguna (ca. 2310-2163 B.C.E.). Daguna was obviously a lady of some social standing since she was able to afford such a splendid lapis lazuli seal. She appears in person on the seal, with her hair neatly dressed and wearing a long pleated robe and several necklaces. Enki/Ea, lord of the sweet waters, is depicted here with fish and floods flowing down from his shoulders (3).

Look out for the unique shell inlay (11) in the same case (ca. 2500-2400 B.C.E.) showing a god fighting a dreadful seven-headed monster with flames spurting out of its back. Seven-headed monsters were very rare in Mesopotamia, but the concept crops up again with the Greek Hydra. In Mesopotamia, such creatures were thought to be the adversaries of the warrior god Ninurta, bringer of rain and fertility. The dragon slayer here, with plants in his crown, may be Ninurta. He has already got the better of one head, which droops lifelessly to the ground. Such inlays were used to decorate small boxes and musical

Female worshipper; Mesopotamia, Sumer, ca. 2700-2500 B.C.E., BLMJ 954

Shell inlay depicting Ninurta battling the seven-headed monster; Mesopotamia, Sumer, ca. 2500-2400 B.C.E., BLMJ 2051

instruments. They were also set into walls as votive plaques or parts of mosaics.

The sun-god Utu/Shamash is shown on a serpentine seal (4) at the beginning of a new day, standing between the two gates of the east where the sun rises every morning, while his attendants open the gates of heaven.

Minor gods and goddesses embodied other powers, such as Nidaba, patroness of writing, or the snake Tishpak, god of healing.

People who hoped for a more intimate relationship with the divine sought a personal god (*lama*) who would guide them, protect them, bring them good fortune and intercede for them with the highest gods. The black seal (15), belonging to a man named Gigire son of Ura, shows a *lama* figure taking a worshipper by the wrist and leading him into the presence of a god seated on his throne.

The gods were crowned with horned diadems. In the wall niche at the end of the gallery you can see a unique relic of a Sumerian cult-statue, a horned cap, probably from the statue of a goddess or god or a deified king. Below the horns is a narrow, dark ring of lapis lazuli which has been partly cleaned. Very little is known about the cult images of ancient Mesopotamia. Almost no trace of them remains, since they were made with cores of perishable organic materials, overlaid with gold, silver and precious stones.

The pedestal vitrine nearby contains two seals from the late Akkadian period (ca. 2246-2160 B.C.E.), portraying major Mesopotamian mythical themes. One seal shows two scenes: one portraying the gods labouring like mortals and a second one depicting the gods fighting one another — just as they did at the beginning of time, before mankind had been created as a convenient labour-saving device so that the gods would not be oppressed with hard work and take their frustrations out on one another.

On the other seal, the hero Etana, the legendary first king of Sumer, ascends to heaven on the back of an

C.

eagle in his quest for the plant of birth which will ensure he has an heir. The end of the story is lost, but since the king list tells us Etana was succeeded by his son, we assume that the childless king found the miraculous plant and a son was born to him. Note the way in which the craftsman has managed to suggest distance — on the ground below, a couple of dogs, a herd of goats and a herdsman stare up in amazement as Etana flies away into the distance.

Turn towards the gallery's rear wall and approach the niche on your right. Here the gods are shown embodied in animal form in the figurines in the right-hand wall case. The Sumerian gods manifested themselves both as humans and as animals. The strength, variety and potency of the animal world seemed especially appropriate to represent the powers of the gods. A wide range of symbolic animals appears in Mesopotamian art.

A. Shell inlay depiciting an eagle; Mesopotamia, Sumer, ca. 2600-2400 B.C.E., BLMJ 2053
B. Impression of cylinder seal, note monkey-like animal sitting on a cushion, playing the flute; Mesopotamia, ca. 2600-2500 B.C.E., BLMJ seal 300
C. Head of male worshipper; Mesopotamia, Sumer, ca. 2700-2600 B.C.E., BLMJ 1323

The bull represented the power to engender, create new life and multiply the herd. Very early on, the disciplined power of the bull became the symbol of divinity, and for three thousand years, from the Early Dynastic period onwards, the gods of Mesopotamia were crowned with bulls' horns. Before that point, it is difficult to recognise which, if any, statues or statuettes may have been divine images.

The polished sculpture of the bearded bull (2) may be a cult image. It stares at the beholder with a weird intensity, suggesting divine power. Its closest parallel is the statue of a recumbent cow from the altar of the temple of the goddess Nintu at Khafaje. Almost all Mesopotamian sculptures of animals are supports, containers or ornaments. Complete animal sculptures like this one, or the bull carved from calcite (3), are most unusual.

You also see the eagle (8), guardian

Head of female worshipper statuette; Mesopotamia, Sumer, ca. 2600-2500 B.C.E., BLMJ 165

Neo-Sumerian stela with a cymbal player; Mesopotamia, ca. 2120-2001 B.C.E., BLMJ 926

Recumbent bull; Mesopotamia, Sumer, ca. 2500-2310 B.C.E., BLMJ 815

of the temple; the lion (10), emblem of the storm gods; and even hybrid creatures, such as the thunderbird, the Imdugud/Anzu (13-15). The Mesopotamians thought that the terrible roar of thunder could only come from a lion's mouth, so they imagined the Anzu with a lion's head.

In the middle wall case the Sumerians themselves are shown at prayer. They stand with clasped hands, gazing intently forward or upward through blind sockets, for their huge inlaid eyes of shell or stone have long since vanished.

Men and women, aristocrats and commoners all set up statuettes like these, representing themselves in prayer and supplication to the gods for themselves and their loved ones. Statuettes like these have been found in the Early Dynastic temples of Mari on the middle Euphrates, in the Diyala region north-east of Baghdad, and in southern Mesopotamia. The lady who seems to have a black eye (3) has lost her original attractive appearance. The bitumen adhesive is all that remains of the eyes of her statue, which would probably have been inlaid with shell and lapis lazuli. On her head she wears an elaborate headdress of stiffened and folded cloth (ca. 2600-2500 B.C.E.).

Although their donors could not spend all their time in the temple, the statuette would offer prayers on their behalf and beg the god or goddess to have mercy on them.

The wall niche to the left contains examples of some of the standard images representing Sumerian kingship. Most of them appear on cylinder seals. The Sumerians understood kingship as an institution created by the gods to guard and guide the people. The king appears as a mighty hunter, crowned monarch and enthroned god, shown overcoming a charging lion (2) — which symbolized terrifying force and unleashed fury. In defeating the wild beasts, the ruler saves his people.

The concept of the king as ruler of the entire world developed under Naram-Sin of Akkade (ca. 2246-2190 B.C.E.). The wall box at the end of the gallery contains a clay tablet recording some of Naram-Sin's royal inscriptions.

The deification of the king was a short-lived phenomenon, lasting only four hundred years. During that period, the kings built temples in their own honour, and were treated as minor gods who despite their divine powers would nonetheless grow old and die.

The copper bowl in the nearby pedestal vitrine describes king Naram-Sin of Akkade (ca. 2246-2190 B.C.E.) as "god of Akkade." The king himself, wearing the horns that symbolized his divine status, can be seen on the wall photograph nearby.

The splendid agate bead in the same pedestal vitrine was dedicated to the goddess Inanna as an offering on behalf of the god-king Shulgi of Ur in the mid-twenty-first century B.C.E., to be hung around the neck of the goddess' statue. The donor of this bead was the priestess Ea-nisha, as recorded in its faintly incised inscription.

The final case, on your right as you leave the gallery, contains examples and depictions of musical instruments used in Sumerian worship — string, percussion and wind instruments. Look out for the shell castanets, decorated with bronze studs. Drums and harps were also played. Music was very important in the Sumerian liturgy. Priests and priestesses praised the gods with songs, poetry and music. They played during the daily banquets of the gods and at special ceremonies. For example, when the temple needed rebuilding (unfortunately a rather common event for the short-lived mud-brick temples of Sumer), the musicians sang special laments to console the deity for the loss of his house until the new shrine was built.

A group of three cylinder seals (8-10) displayed in the same case depict the date harvest celebrations, one of the many Sumerian festivals.

Sumerian religion stressed humanity's worship of the gods and the blessings the gods give to humanity in this world. According to the Sumerians, the afterlife was a mournful twilight, where the dead moped in the dust and lived on ashes. There was little incentive to prepare for the life to come. The gods and goddesses would reward one's good deeds by blessings in this life.

Impression of a cylinder seal showing gods building a tower; Mesopotamia, ca. 2246-2160 B.C.E., BLMJ Seal 377

GALLERY 7

OLD KINGDOM EGYPT

And Joseph commanded his servants the physicians to embalm his father. And the physicians embalmed Israel. And forty days were fulfilled for the days of embalming.
(Genesis 50:2 3)

Most archaeological remains of Old Kingdom Egypt come from buildings prepared for eternity, such as pyramids and officials' tombs. The towns of this period are almost irretrievable, since they are buried deep beneath the villages of modern Egypt. Many aspects of everyday life are therefore unknown to us.

The Egyptians' dedication to preparing for the afterlife should not lead one to imagine them as obsessed and made wretched by the thought of death. Rather, they anticipated the afterworld as an opportunity to continue everyday life at its most delightful, complete with parties and family outings.

For the spirit to survive in the afterworld, the Egyptians held that the body must be preserved. The process of mummification involved removing organs liable to rot, drying out the rest of the body, and making the corpse look as lifelike as possible. The forty-day period referred to in the Bible is the approximate length of the dessication process (see the wall panel in the far corner).

The earliest evidence of mummification using this method is roughly contemporary with the Great Pyramid. The burial equipment of King Cheops' mother includes a chest with special compartments for her mummified inner organs. Before the Fourth Dynasty, it seems that mummification entailed simply wrapping the body in bandages soaked in natron to dry out the flesh. By the time Jacob was mummified, the practice was already a thousand years old.

In the centre of this gallery, we have reconstructed the royal burial ground at Giza as it was at the end of the Fourth Dynasty (ca. 2500 B.C.E.), soon after the pyramid of Mycerinus (Menkaure in the original Egyptian) was completed. You can see the burial complexes of Cheops (Khufu), Chephren (Khafre) and Mycerinus, the city which grew up to service the priests and officials who worked there, and the access harbour. Apart from the pyramid itself, the royal burial complex included a pyramid temple (see the key to the model), where food and drink were offered to sustain the king's spirit; a valley temple, probably for the mummification ceremonies; and a covered causeway linking the two temples. After the burial rites, the dead king, united with the gods, would continue to bless the people of Egypt.

During the Old Kingdom, non-royal Egyptians did not anticipate spending their afterlife with the gods in the same way, although sometimes tomb-owners threatened to sue anyone who damaged their tomb "in the presence of the great god". An Egyptian official dreamed of a life of leisure, with all the pleasures of eating, drinking, hunting, music and family life. However, food and drink must be provided regularly if the dead person were not to starve. Usually people arranged for sacrifices to be offered after their death, but they supplemented them by covering the walls of their offering chapels with pictures of servants bringing or preparing food (see wall panel showing the tomb-chapel of Nefer).

Magically activated by the burial

False door from the tomb of Impey; Egypt, Saqqara, ca. 2220-2172 B.C.E., BLMJ 1056

Relief from the tomb of Akhtihotep; Egypt, Saqqara, ca. 2650-2550 B.C.E., BLMJ 1101

ceremonies, these pictures would supply the dead person with everything they needed. The rare wall-paintings of offering-bearers from the late Sixth Dynasty displayed in the wall case to the left of the wall panel, show typical objects they would carry — trays of figs, loaves or cakes, and pots of wine and milk. The delights of the natural world were also available in the next world: one painting (2) shows a boatman bringing lotus blossoms for the tomb owner. Some objects would have been used in everyday life and also deposited in tombs for the owner's use in the afterlife — a wooden headrest (9) to serve as a pillow, two alabaster pots (6, 8) for ointments and a black stone bowl (7).

The tomb-owner would also appeal to passers-by to make food offerings to him. The offerings were placed in front of his statue. This acted as a dwelling-place for the spirit, a splendid substitute body showing him resplendent with youth, strength and energy. The statue of Mereruka (ca. 2330 B.C.E.), still in place in his tomb-chapel at Saqqara, is a typical example (see colour panel on wall).

In case the mummy decayed or was destroyed, substitutes were included for the body in the tomb.

The most important substitute body was the statue of the tomb-owner, but any picture could house the person's spirit, such as the elegant relief of Akhtihotep, priest of Bastet, from his tomb-chapel in Saqqara (ca. 2650-2550 B.C.E.). Akhtihotep is dressed in a leopard skin, complete with tail — worn by certain types of priests. It would originally have been painted with spots.

The nearby pedestal vitrine displays two more relief fragments from tombs, including a son represented very much smaller than life-size at his mother's feet.

Another focus for the offering cult was the false door, a wall decoration which combined a stylised door and a picture of the tomb-owner feasting. The dead person's spirit was believed to emerge from the central niche and enjoy the offerings. These were not burnt or destroyed: the priest took them home as his salary. The false door here, to the left of the entrance to Gallery 9, belonged to a Sixth Dynasty priest of Ptah named Impey. He is shown seated at an offering-table, anticipating "a thousand (helpings of) bread, beer, cake, beef, fowl, alabaster vessels and clothing".

Leaving ancient Egypt, we now enter the world of third millennium Anatolia (modern Turkey) and Iran.

The wall case to the right of the entrance to Gallery 8 contains burnished red jugs with vertical spouts (1-5), from the third and early second millennia in western Anatolia. The spherical body contains large amounts of liquid, the stubby vertical spout makes pouring easy, and the short rope-like handles are very sturdy. The long ribbon handles, on the other hand, are easier to grasp.

With the passage of time, the spouts grow longer and more shapely. Notice the cut-away spouts, which may have served as cradles to rest the spout of another container when filling the jug. These jugs are found all over western and central Anatolia during the early second millennium, and even in Cilicia and the eastern Aegean islands. On the extreme left stands a large painted jar from Cappadocia (eastern Turkey).

The miniature pots, also from western Anatolia, were found in graves — they may have been symbolic vessels produced for the dead, or perhaps children's toys. Some of these black pots contained a reddish-orange substance, maybe ochre, used as make-up.

For a closer view of these vessels, and to read their labels, enter Gallery 8 and look at the case from the other side.

Returning to the last case in Gallery 7, you can see examples of the beautiful painted pottery of third millennium Iran: storage jars decorated with swooping birds of prey and stylised horned animals. Vessels like these, made all over Iran, are part of a long tradition of painted pottery.

GALLERY 8

THE HARRIET & LEON POMERANCE GALLERY

GENESIS 14, THE AGE OF WARFARE

And it came to pass in the days of Amraphel king of Shinar, Arioch king of Ellasar, Chedorlaomer king of Elam, and Tidal king of Goiim that they made war with Bera king of Sodom, and with Birsha king of Gomorrah, Shinab king of Admah, and Shemeber king of Zeboiim, and the king of Bela...
(Genesis 14:1-2).

Genesis 14 (the war between the Four Kings and the Five Kings) describes a situation which was characteristic of the Near East during the Middle Bronze Age, the period to which some scholars date the Patriarchs. The Levant was divided into many city-states, each ruled by a different king. These petty kings made war on one another and raided each other's territory. Migrations of various peoples, such as the Amorites and later the Hittites, disrupted society on a large scale, and posed a threat to more settled peoples.

This gallery displays weapons from all over the Near East, from the late third to mid-second millennia. Warfare during this period was conducted by soldiers wielding swords and axes such as these. As protection against attack, kings fortified their cities with massive defence walls and earthworks. Military hardware grew more and more sophisticated. Bronze replaced the softer copper as the main material for weapons, increasing their striking power. The new closed casting moulds made it possible for axeheads, spearheads and arrowheads to be mass-produced, so a ruler could equip his army far more quickly than in the past.

The first wall niche on the left displays weapons found in the Levant, of the type used by the Amorites and Canaanites (see also the wall panel to the left of the case). The Amorite warriors of the Levant were buried with their weapons — short swords, spears, daggers, bows and arrows and axes. This selection allowed them to fight at any distance — bows and arrows (2) for long-range fighting, spears (5, 6) to throw from a distance of several metres, and swords and daggers (7) for hand-to-hand combat. At this period, the curved sword (8) was used as a slashing weapon.

The main weapon, however, was the axe. The most popular type of axe in the Middle Bronze Age was the "duckbill" axehead with elliptical holes (1, 2). Its broad blade was most efficient when used against unprotected enemies. The tiny model of a fenestrated axehead (3) was an offering from a warrior's grave. The duckbill axe was later replaced by the long, narrow chisel-shaped axe (4), which was more effective in piercing body armour. The small clay model (10) shows a bearded warrior holding a curved sword and a fenestrated axe just like the actual examples shown in this case.

In Mesopotamia, warring city-states had been struggling to gain control of the region and its resources ever since the early third millennium. From the very beginning of the Early Dynastic period, the cities were defended by huge walls, and weapon technology began to develop (see the next wall panel to the right). The Mesopotamians not only

Fenestrated axeheads; Levant, ca. 2000-1750 B.C.E., BLMJ 469, 471

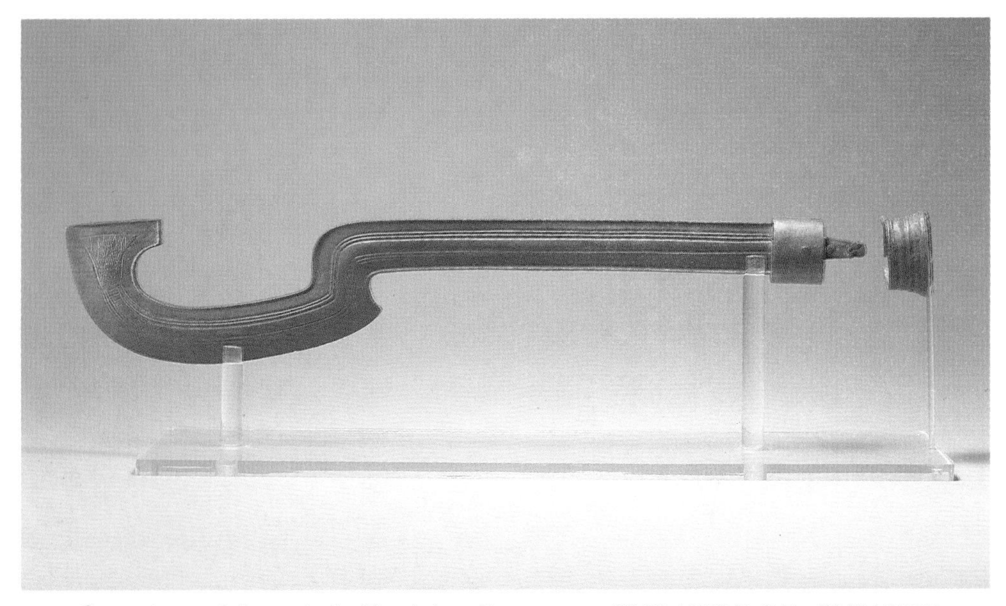

Curved sword decorated with a lotus; Canaan, ca. 2000-1550 B.C.E., BLMJ 2767

Clay warrior holding a curved sword and a fenestrated axe; Syria, ca. 1900-1750 B.C.E., BLMJ 2763

feuded with one another, but had to fend off raiding barbarians who came to ravage the rich cities of the plain — the tribes of the Zagros mountains from the north, the Elamites from the east and the Amorites from the west. The Mesopotamian weapons displayed in the central wall niche may have been used by actual warriors, like the examples from the Levant, or they may be ceremonial weapons to be carried in sacred processions. Like the early Egyptians, the early Mesopotamians fought with maces. The white stone macehead shown here (2), which is decorated with three animals, was probably for ritual display.

The Mesopotamians often cast axeheads with a vertical hole for the shaft (3). This made the weapon much stronger, since it decreased the chances that the axe-head would fly off the handle on impact. In the Early Dynastic and Akkadian periods (ca. 2600-2200 B.C.E.) socketed axes like the one shown here became standard equipment for the Mesopotamian fighter. The epsilon-shaped axe (6) was particularly popular in Syria and Canaan in this period (the early third millennium). Later, it was supplanted by the fenestrated axe. Bows and arrows were also used, as can be seen on the cylinder seal (4) exhibited here.

The area of Anatolia was particularly affected by mass migrations from southeastern Europe and across the Caucasian mountains. As far back as history records, the cities of the area were at war either with one another or against invading peoples. Again, the cities were defended by powerful fortifications and weapons became stronger and more diversified in order to repulse different groups of invaders (see wall panel to the right).

The Anatolians had a particularly well-developed tradition of metallurgy. They experimented with alloys which allowed them to produce types of bronze with different hardness and different melting points, such as arsenical bronze, tin bronze and zinc bronze. Using the "lost wax" process, they produced swords, maceheads, spearheads with tangs, arrowheads, axeblades and daggers. They knew how to rivet metal weapon heads to their handles, and how to work sheet metal.

In the third wall case, to the right, you can see typical Anatolian lugged axeheads (4) and early shafthole axeheads which could be wedged on to the handle (1,2). One of these is made of polished stone, imitating the shape of a metal axehead. Stone imitations of metal axes were common when metal was first introduced, since it was still an expensive luxury material. Unlike the Mesopotamian examples, later metal axeheads (5, 6) have a tang projecting from the bottom of the axehead to support the shaft. Crescent-shaped axeheads, distantly related to the Mesopotamian type, were also used (3). Rather unusually, the original rivet that fastened this example to the shaft has been preserved. A distinctive type of spearhead (7) has a long narrow tang (broken off here) and two holes for binding it to the shaft. The bronze figure (8) represents a warrior, naked except for his helmet and belt, who would have originally grasped weapons, like the example shown on the wall panel to the left.

In the pedestal vitrine on the way into the next gallery are faces from the early second millennium B.C.E. — typical baked clay female portrait heads, each with a distinctive character. Several of them have elaborate hairstyles with dozens of tiny plaits, and they still bear traces of black and red paint. Statues of the head alone are very unusual in the ancient Near East. Scholars suggest that they are sculptors' models, or votive offerings from an important shrine — perhaps portraits of the donors.

GALLERY 9

THE AGE OF THE PATRIARCHS

Thus says the Lord, the God of Israel, "Your fathers lived of old beyond the Euphrates, Terah, the father of Abraham and of Nahor; and they served other gods. Then I took your father Abraham from beyond the river and led him through all the land of Canaan and made his offspring many."
(Joshua 24:2-3)

This gallery outlines the religious beliefs held in Mesopotamia, Syria, Canaan and Egypt at the beginning of the second millennium B.C.E. — the backdrop to Abram's religious quest.

As you enter the gallery, a decorated bronze beaker from northern Mesopotamia (in a pedestal vitrine) gives you a glimpse of scenes from life in the second millennium B.C.E. These include a king sitting on a throne (top right), holding a beaker very similar to this one, men leading and carrying animals, and in the lower register, three singing girls and a man riding on an ass.

The large cuneiform tablet in the first wall niche (to the left as you enter) in this gallery opens a window onto the everyday routine of Babylonian temples. It comes from the city of Larsa, midway between Babylon and the mouth of the Euphrates, and is dated to the second year of Rim-Sin, last king of Larsa (ca. 1821 B.C.E.), just before Hammurabi of Babylon conquered the city.

This unique text describes the daily rituals of the temple during the ten days from the fifteenth to the twenty-fourth of the month of Shabatu. The present Hebrew calendar is based on the Mesopotamian lunar calendar, so this month is the equivalent of the Hebrew month Shevat. In ancient Babylon, the fifteenth of Shevat was the day on which it was decided whether or not to insert an extra month of Adar into the calendar. Since at that point the barley harvest was 45 days away in Nisan, this decision was vitally important for the agricultural cycle. On that day, the priests ascended to the roof of the temple in solemn procession to observe the evening rising of Venus, the starting-point of their astronomical calculations (see the reconstruction in colour). They prayed and offered sacrifices to Venus, who at that time was believed to be Ninsianna, the astral aspect of the goddess Inanna/Ishtar. As she rose in the sky, the Mesopotamians imagined her looking down on humankind and judging the cases of the just and the unjust.

The inscribed stone plaque (7) in the same case also comes from Larsa, and is roughly contemporary with the tablet. It is the foundation stone of a temple dedicated to Inanna.

Look out for the plaque (4) showing two high-hatted men squaring off against each other with clashing sticks. They were probably athletes, participating in games during certain festivals, or dancers performing a war-dance in honour of Ishtar, goddess of war. Just to the left, a small bronze figure (2) illustrates the position the Babylonians adopted for prayer in the second millennium B.C.E. — kneeling on one knee with a hand raised towards the face, and sometimes touching the nose. This was very different from the Sumerian position for prayer, which consisted of standing with the hands clasped over the stomach.

Tablet with Shevat ritual observances; Babylonia, Larsa, ca. 1821 B.C.E., BLMJ 3127

Family; Syria, ca. 2000-1550 B.C.E., BLMJ 2086

In a nearby pedestal vitrine is another cuneiform tablet, about 140 years younger than the Larsa temple tablet. It records a building inscription of king Ammiditana of Babylon. Some of the phrases he uses are reminiscent of the Psalms: "...to shepherd proudly the ... people of my country in secure pastures and watering places, and to let them lie in safe pastures...". Below the tablet is a small green seal dedicated to the god of justice on behalf of Hammurabi of Babylon — a fitting gesture to honour the promulgator of one of the most detailed law codes of the ancient Near East. Although the law code of Hammurabi is perhaps the most famous, he was following a centuries-old tradition. Ur-Nammu, founder of the Third Dynasty of Ur, is credited with the first preserved legal code.

The pedestal vitrine next to this shows how religious ideas from Mesopotamia percolated into Syria. The "flowing vase" held by these bronze goddesses was a common Mesopotamian symbol of abundance.

In the wall niche to the right are bronze and clay figurines from the early second millennium in the Levant (ca. 2000-1550 B.C.E.). They may have functioned as votive offerings, representing the worshipper who offered them, or they may be popular versions of certain major divinities. Remnants of metal jewellery have survived on some examples in other collections — rings on the perforations of the headdresses and gold-plated studs inserted in the navel.

The women's slim waists (17) would be the envy of many a modern dieter, although their prominent navels and broad hips, promising fertility, are probably less fashionable. One figure wears an elaborate floppy hat, another a turban. One figure is two-headed (2), probably an abbreviated version of cult figures which show two deities seated side by side on a chair.

The Syrian cylinder seals (6-8) displayed here show local gods and goddesses, probably similar to those worshipped in Canaan at this time.

Look closely at the two cult vessels from northern Syria (1,19). The first is in the form of a woman wearing elaborate jewellery, who supports her breasts with her hands and carries a lamp on her head. The second vessel consists of a bowl with a tall foot, and is decorated with incised "tree of life" patterns.

Moving along to the next wall niche, to the right, you can see objects used in daily life in Canaan and the neighbouring countries at the time of Abraham. They include elaborate clay vessels — note the jug with a smiling woman perched precariously on top (18). The only aperture is a very small hole on her left shoulder, so this object may have been used as a rattle rather than for pouring liquids. The little shelf holds four lively figurines (10-13) made of bronze and clay, including a strange being (an ape?) wearing a necklace.

Three haematite cylinder seals (7-9) demonstrate the curious mixture of Egyptian elements (e.g. the *ankh* on seal 8) and Mesopotamian motifs (e.g. the palm tree on seal 7) that is so typical of Levantine art. Basalt, a black volcanic stone found locally, was used for sculpture (2) and for making household implements such as the mortar shown here (1).

Turning around and walking back a little way, you will find a pedestal vitrine with stone moulds for casting metal plaques, portraying naked goddesses covered with jewellery. Moulds like this one, and figures produced from them, are found all the way from Troy in western Anatolia to Sippar, north of Babylonia on the Euphrates. The distribution of these figures implies that the moulds belonged to travelling smiths, perhaps journeying with merchants, who produced identical pieces for customers in far-flung regions. These three ladies are nameless, but they may well be the three daughters of the Canaanite god Baal, patron of the land and fertility.

Stone jewellery mould for lead figurines; Anatolia, ca. 1810-1740 B.C.E., BLMJ 953

In the same vitrine is a variety of superbly finished stamp seals, decorated with geometric patterns and other designs — note the tiny pin-figures on the Hittite seal (4), which represent the storm-god Teshub and other deities.

With the next pedestal vitrine, we leap to the other end of the Fertile Crescent — Iran, represented here by a beautifully worked ritual goblet carved with a rampant ibex (or ram), and a rather crudely worked cylinder seal.

Continuing our tour through the Near East, we now come to Egypt, where preparations for the afterlife continued to preoccupy people's imaginations; many Old Kingdom practices formerly restricted to the pharaoh became available to the elite and well-to-do during the First Intermediate Period and early Middle Kingdom (ca. 2100-2000 B.C.E.).

From the late Old Kingdom onwards,

models of servants were often placed in tombs as a supplement to the reliefs, to ensure the tomb-owner and his family the services of a brewer or baker in the afterlife. In the Eleventh Dynasty, these models developed to the point where they included scenes of entire workshops. In the slaughterhouse in the pedestal vitrine near the coffin, a steer is being killed to provide tasty fresh meat for the tomb-owner. One butcher slits the animal's throat with a huge knife; the other originally held a bowl to catch the spurts of blood. Note that the animal is not slaughtered by an axe or mace but by slitting its throat to let the blood escape, reminiscent of the Jewish method of slaughtering. Whereas the Jews refrained from drinking the blood, and poured it out in sacrifice, the Egyptians also held the blood in esteem but apparently prepared it as blood pudding and ate it. The other two servants are probably making beer, the favourite drink of the Egyptians. We would doubtless not like Egyptian-style beer; it was made from fermented dough and was very lumpy.

This beautiful wooden coffin at the far end of the gallery comes from Meir in Middle Egypt, and belonged to the steward Tjetetu, a low-level administrator. It is decorated with a striking stylised facade, repeated all round the coffin, and with the two holy eyes of the god Horus, which magically enabled the dead person to see out. Inside the lid, invisible to the viewer, is spell 335 of the Coffin Texts, intended to identify the dead person with various gods: "...I will go forth upon the road which I know in the direction of the island of the just... I will arrive at the land of the horizon-dwellers in them, I will go forth from the sacred doorway...".

In the wall niche near the gallery exit is a model of a boat (2), made to allow its owner to travel in comfort on the rivers of the afterworld. In the same case are a

Painted wooden coffin; Egypt, Meir, ca. 1963-1875 B.C.E., BLMJ 1098

Wooden model of a slaughterhouse; Egypt, ca. 2106-1787 B.C.E., BLMJ 2678

few fertility figurines (3) found in temples, houses and also tombs, as a promise of pleasures in this life or the next, scantily dressed but decked out in jewellery and elaborate wigs. The Egyptians were most partial to wigs and saw them as an important addition to an exciting love life. The wicked woman in an Egyptian parallel to the story of Joseph quotes the innocent hero as propositioning her with the words, "Come on, let's spend an hour making love! Get your wig on!".

The wall boxes on the opposite side of the gallery, to the right of the entrance to Gallery 5, show small figurines of the main gods of Egypt. Some of these are city gods, like Ptah (1), his lion-headed wife Sekhmet (4,5,7) and their son Nefertum of Memphis, or Amun (13), his wife Mut and their son Khons (16) of Thebes, brought together in the nuclear family arrangements so dear to the Egyptians. Others are popular gods like Bes (23-25), patron of dancing and music, who watched over pregnant women and small children.

Many of these deities belong to the two major mythical cycles of the Egyptians. One set of myths describes the sun god's journey through the underworld at night (see the wall panel above the wall boxes), comforting the spirits of the just, renewing the tortures of the damned, and confronting his eternal enemy, the chaos-snake Apophis, who threatens to engulf the sun and deprive the world of light. During this journey, the sun-god is rejuvenated and at dawn he is reborn as a baby.

The other mythological cycle revolves around the figure of the god Osiris (26), murdered by his evil brother Seth. It describes the efforts of Osiris' faithful wife Isis (27) to restore him to life, and his son Horus' (29) struggle to regain his rightful kingdom.

To the left of the wall boxes, the temples of ancient Egypt are represented by a large colour photograph of the hypostyle hall in the temple of Hathor at Dendera (see accompanying wall panel for details of the temple ritual). The fragments of wall paintings here show lector-priests, who were responsible for reading the sacred texts used in the rituals. The Egyptian name for these priests, *herihebt*, is indirectly related to the Hebrew word *hartumim*, which is used in the Bible to describe the "magicians" summoned by Pharaoh to compete with the miracles performed by Moses and Aaron. This would have been quite natural, since lector-priests were traditionally supposed to be skilled in magic of all kinds.

At the very end of the gallery, our tour takes a leap to Crete. The double axe displayed here was a typical symbol of the great commercial civilization of Minoan Crete, which at this period was expanding across the Aegean, as far as the Levant. The stone vessels here, which would have been laboriously worked by rubbing the stone with abrasives, may have held cosmetics or precious ointments and perfumes.

WALKWAY

Galleries 9 and 10 are linked by a short walkway. Immediately to your left as you leave Gallery 9 is a life-size statue of Ramesses II (1290-1224 B.C.E.), enthroned here in splendour. He may have been the pharaoh of the Exodus or the Oppression. Seated on his chair of state, he is very much the king and conqueror, his feet planted on nine lines, representing the Nine Bows, traditional symbols of the enemies of Egypt.

Next to it is an unfinished wall-painting of a married couple receiving offerings, originally part of the decoration of a tomb chapel. Look closely and you will see how the design has been sketched out in reddish brown paint, and the first wash of brown for the flesh and white for the garments has been applied. The details of the faces, limbs, costumes and so on have not yet been added.

The last exhibit in the walkway is a massive sarcophagus lid made of pink granite. It comes from central Egypt, a rather provincial area, and is not quite as elegant in style and proportions as the examples from bigger Egyptian centres. It must have been its owner's pride and joy, as it would have cost a large amount of money, and would have signalled his importance and wealth. Beneath the hands, Nut, the goddess of heaven, kneels with her wings spread protectively over the dead man.

GALLERY 10

WHEN ISRAEL SOJOURNED IN EGYPT

And God spoke to Israel... "I am God, the God of thy father. Fear not to go down into Egypt; for I will make of thee a great nation. I will go down with thee into Egypt; and I will also surely bring thee up again."
(Genesis 46:2-4)

In Gallery 10, we go on a tour of the Near East at the time of the Exodus. The superpowers of the time were Egypt and its rivals, the Mitanni and Hittites. The Egyptians had finally succeeded in expelling the alien Hyksos rulers, who had controlled northern Egypt during the second quarter of the second millennium B.C.E., and were enjoying a period of unrivalled prosperity. The rival Mitanni empire of Anatolia and northern Syria was superseded in the mid-fourteenth century B.C.E. by the Hittites.

We start with a brief look at the New Kingdom in Egypt (1542-1070 B.C.E.). In the first wall niche on the left is an assortment of items, most of which were placed in tombs to enhance the owner's "quality of afterlife". Fragments of wall-paintings show a mummy (8), a procession of servants carrying chairs into the tomb (5) and a couple wearing jewellery (3). To the left is a funerary cone (10), a decorative element from a tomb façade. Next to it is a rare late Seventeenth Dynasty statue of Iahhotep (8). Strangely enough, this name was usually given to women; this man may have been named after queen Ahhotep, who played a major role in the Egyptians' liberation struggle against the Hyksos. The limestone pots (6,9) next to the statue are painted to resemble much more expensive granite vessels.

The next group of exhibits illustrates different Egyptian boats, the main means of transport in Egypt.

The second wall niche includes a variety of cosmetic items — stone kohl-pots (13,15) which held black eye-paint made of pounded soot mixed with grease, a bronze razor (17), alabaster perfume containers (12,14) and glass perfume bottles (7,8). Jewellery included brightly coloured faience beads (1), crystal earrings (5) and rings (16).

Prosperous Egyptians would have stored their wine in jars like the example shown here (6), painted with flower petals. Flowers, especially the lotus, were popular in Egyptian art and can be seen here on the faience vessels (10, 11) and in the wall-paintings showing guests at a party (2) and a funeral (9).

As is evident from these objects, Egypt during the New Kingdom was at its most prosperous. Exotic wares and raw materials flooded in from all corners of the empire. No wonder that the Israelites, in the wilds of the Sinai, pined for the fleshpots of Egypt — forgetting that their share in these fleshpots had been tiny.

In the pedestal vitrine near the case are three ivory cosmetic spoons, carved in charming forms — a swimming girl, a bound oryx and a bull's leg.

Between the second and third wall niches is a section of a stone relief from a tomb chamber, showing the weighing of the heart. The contemporary Mesopotamians and ancient Israelites envisaged the dead as condemned to a miserable afterlife in a dark dingy underworld. The Egyptians, by contrast, believed that their fate in the next world depended on their behaviour in this life. After death, their heart, the seat of their conscience and personality, would be weighed against the symbol of righteousness, the figure of the goddess

Akhenaten; Egypt, ca. 1353-1335 B.C.E., BLMJ 2680

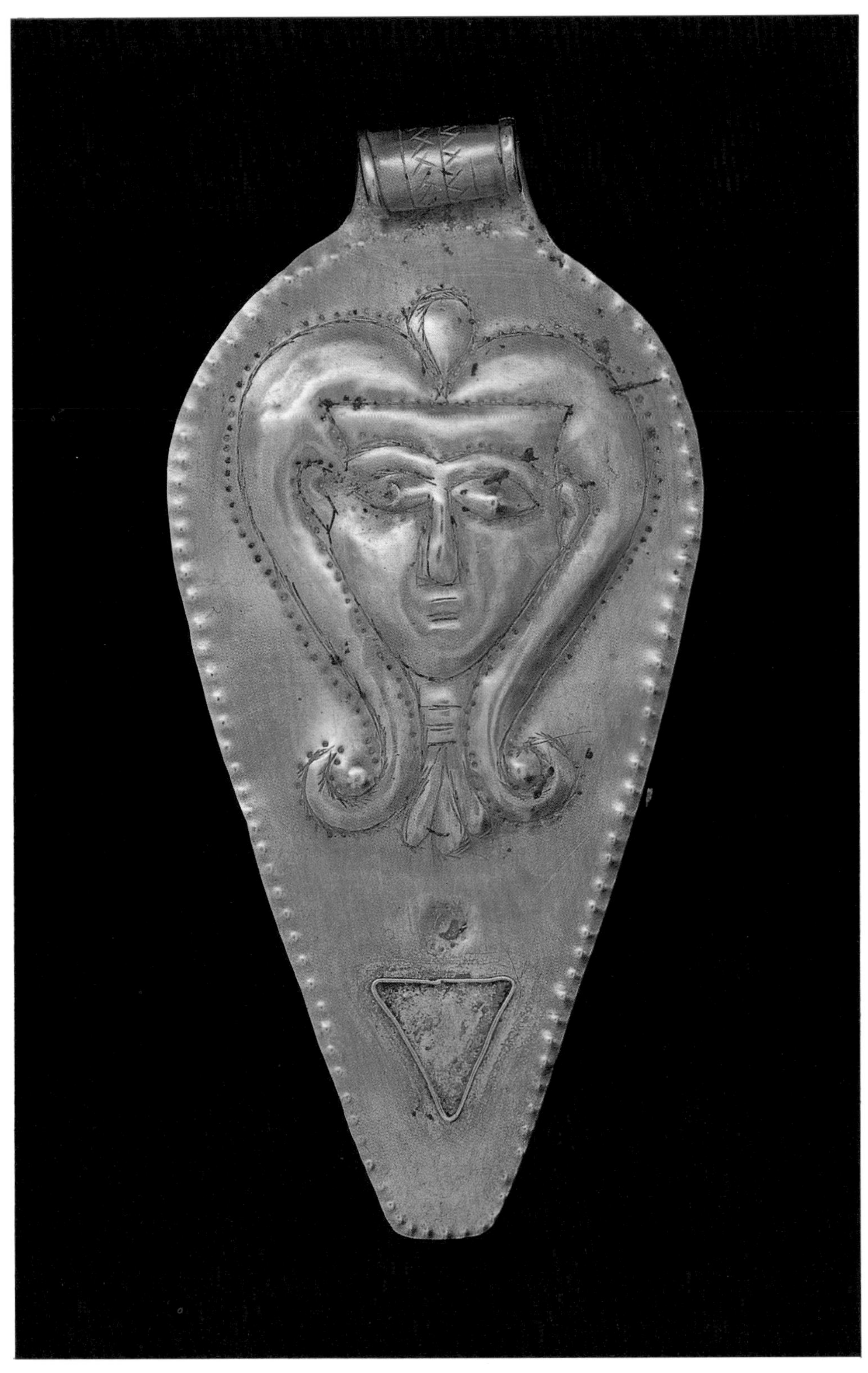

Pendant depicting Canaanite fertility goddess; Canaan, ca. 1500-1300 B.C.E., BLMJ 1345

Maat. If the dead person was an evildoer, his or her heart would be fed to the monster lurking below the scales — a terrifying mixture of hippopotamus, crocodile and lion. If the dead person had done good, the gods led them into the presence of Osiris, who welcomed them into heaven.

Nearby stands a black granite stela. It belonged to Wennofer, a humble scribe of Osiris, who crowded every single one of his brothers, sisters, sons and daughters onto it in order to ensure their share in the offering cult.

Not only gracious living flourished in the New Kingdom but also theological speculation. The pharaoh Akhenaten (1353-1335 B.C.E.) devoted himself to the exclusive worship of the sun-disk Aten, built a brand-new city in his honour at el-Amarna, and destroyed the names and images of other gods. Under Akhenaten's inspiration, his artists evolved a striking new style combining naturalistic and stylised elements, as shown in the blocks in the third wall niche. The main motif showed the Aten's rays pouring blessings on Akhenaten and his wife Nefertiti as they sacrificed to the god. Other scenes showed the king participating in religious rites (4), processions and reward ceremonies. The blocks in this case show people who lived at el-Amarna: grooms (7), fan-bearers (2,6) and minor courtiers (3). In the centre of the case, Akhenaten himself gazes out at the world with his characteristic dreamy eye.

Akhenaten's hymns to his god address him as the sole god, the creator of all beings. In other ways, however, the Aten is far less involved with his creatures than the God of the Hebrews (or other deities of the ancient Near East). It is not said that he heals the sick, rescues the poor or forgives sinners. Interestingly enough, Akhenaten retained a few traditional Egyptian concepts, as illustrated by the *ushabti* shown here (1), which would stand in for the dead king in performing menial labour in the afterlife.

Akhenaten's shocking innovations earned him the hatred of future generations. Thirty years after his death, he was known as "the criminal", and the Egyptians tried to wipe out every trace of him from the historical record. His temples were demolished, his name and face erased from his reliefs, and his city blotted from the map. The beautiful face of pink stone in this case was found smashed into splinters by some enemy of the "heretic king".

By the reign of Ramesses II, some 50 years later, Egyptian orthodoxy was back in the saddle, as exemplified by the fragment of a statue showing Ramesses II and the obscure earth god Tatenen, to whom the king was very partial.

The objects in the next wall case to the right reflect themes connected with the story of the Exodus: the power of the pharaohs, their building activities — which may have involved Hebrew labour — and their gods, who could not prevent the Israelites' departure.

There are two different theories about the dating of the Exodus. One involves counting back 480 years from the dedication of Solomon's temple (1 Kings 6:1) in about 966 B.C.E. This would place the Exodus at about 1446 B.C.E., midway through the Eighteenth Dynasty.

The other theory dates the Exodus by the names of the store-cities which the Israelites were forced to build, Pithom and Ramses. These can be identified as Per-Itum ("the house of Atum"), modern Tell el-Mashkuta and Pi-Ramesses ("the house of Ramesses"), modern Qantir in the eastern Delta. Building began at Pi-Ramesses at the end of the Eighteenth Dynasty, but it was Ramesses II who moved his capital to the new city and began to build there on a gigantic scale.

At Pi-Ramesses, Ramesses' court lived in splendour. His courtiers, as you see in the wall painting (3), wore eye-catching jewellery and elegant pleated garments.

Ramesses was an energetic ruler and undertook extensive building projects throughout Egypt. Each new building would have been endowed with a deposit of bricks marked with the king's name (4, 5) and small symbolic representations of sacrificial offerings (2) placed in the foundations.

When he was young and belligerent, Ramesses marched his armies out of the eastern Delta to campaign in Syria, following the example of his predecessors. After many years of strife, Ramesses made a peace treaty with the Hittites, the other superpower of that period, and brought peace to the Middle East for more than fifty years. By building, warmongering and bringing peace and prosperity to his country, Ramesses had done all that the Egyptians and their gods expected of a king.

The Bible, however, views history differently. The seemingly omnipotent ruler of the most powerful nation on earth is made anonymous, a mere foil for the mighty deeds of God and His servant Moses. God's interest is in the Israelites, the lowly brick-makers and builders.

From the Egyptian point of view, this anonymity would have been most odd; the pharaohs devoted a great deal of effort to perpetuating their names and the memory of their deeds. Objects bearing the pharaoh's name, such as the scarabs or ring bezels made in the moulds displayed here (1-4, 6-9 in the centre of the case) were mass-produced and could have been owned even by the poorest Egyptians. Ramesses II carved his name not only on his own monuments (5), but in a rather cavalier way, over the names of his predecessors on their temples and statues.

Servants, slaves and workers are seldom commemorated in Egyptian records. Perhaps we can compare the Israelites with the figure of the Semitic prisoner (1), carved on a sandstone relief. He was once part of a long string of captives tied at their elbows and throats, personifications of places which the king had conquered. A real prisoner would probably be sent to work in a factory owned by a temple, less often sold or given to an owner. If he was lucky, he might be freed.

At the extreme right of the case are depictions of two of the most important Egyptian deities. Hathor (2) is shown as a cow emerging from the "Western Mountain", the realm of the dead, against a background of her sacred plant, the papyrus. As a mother goddess, she enabled the dead to be reborn into the afterlife. Re-Harakhty (1), god of the morning sun rising on the horizon, is shown on a stela, being worshipped by a military official.

Leaving Egypt, we now turn to the Levant, with a splendid example of a bronze spearhead in the nearby pedestal vitrine. The heads of boars that decorate the base of the blade show that this spear was specially designed for hunting wild boar. The heads also served a practical purpose: they would have caught on the ribs of the quarry and prevented it from charging up the spear shaft in an attempt to gore the hunter.

The people who made this beautiful spearhead may have belonged to the Hurrians. They formed part of the Mitannian empire in the second millennium B.C.E. This was a great confederation of peoples which stretched from the eastern coast of the Mediterranean to the Zagros mountains in the east, ruled by an Indo-European aristocracy who had come as nomads from the north and had settled in Mitanni. The chariot warrior (*marjanu*) was a key figure in Mitannian culture, rather like the knight in mediaeval society. Their chariots are depicted on the cylinder seals (2) in the next pedestal vitrine. A tiny bronze chariot (1) drawn by two mules has spoked wheels, thought to have been invented along with chariot warfare by Mitannian warriors at this period. The model also shows the small platform on which the warrior stood while his steeds charged forward at full tilt.

The Mitannian empire disintegrated in about 1350 B.C.E., under mounting

Ivory furniture inlay in the form of the god Bes; Egypt, ca. 1391-1323 B.C.E., BLMJ 771

pressure from the surrounding empires — the Egyptian, the Hittite, and the newly independent Middle Assyrian dynasty in northern Mesopotamia. As a result the Hittites again played an aggressive role in the Near East. From the mid-fourteenth to the early thirteenth centuries B.C.E., they fought the Egyptians for control of Lebanon and Syria. The best-known engagement was the Battle of Qadesh (about 1285 B.C.E.) on the River Orontes in Syria, between Ramesses II of Egypt and Muwatalli of Hatti. The relief (12) in the case to the left

Hathor in the form of a cow; Egypt, Thebes, ca. 1307-1196 B.C.E., BLMJ 1148

Gaming board; Canaan, ca. 1500 B.C.E., BLMJ 1996, 1997, Gift of Christine Schmid in honour of Elsa Schmid-Schmid

of the entrance to Gallery 12 shows a Hittite charioteer and the horse from the following chariot, part of one of Ramesses' reliefs commemorating his great victory at Qadesh. The battle could more accurately be described as a no-score draw, but modesty was never Ramesses II's strong point. The Hittite forces used axes of the type exhibited here (9-11, 13) against Ramesses II's army. Stamp seal 7 to the right shows a tiny figure of a striding god, carrying a bow and wearing the tall hat typical of Hittite deities (15). Both men's and women's names appear on seals here.

The case to the right takes us to the disputed area of Syria and Canaan (see map). Bronze figurines (6-11) and cylinder seals show the variety of gods worshipped by the Canaanites and their neighbours at the time of the Israelites' arrival.The deities are depicted enthroned, or with their arms raised to strike. Other bronzes portray Syrians and Anatolians dressed in long robes. Five cuneiform tablets from the Syrian site of Emar in the Hittite territories (12-16) give us rare glimpses into contemporary life. One records the desire of a man called Abiu son of Zikria to ensure the support of his wife, Hudi daughter of Nai-Dagan, after his death.

The pedestal vitrine nearby holds gold and silver jewellery, including two plaques (1, 2) depicting Astarte, goddess of love and fertility. She is shown naked, with her hair styled in the fashion of the Egyptian goddess Hathor.

In the next pedestal vitrine is a Canaanite board game (ca. 1500 B.C.E.), complete with pieces and knucklebones used as dice. Like most board games in the ancient world, this game involved moving one's pieces round and finally off the board while trying to block one's opponent from doing so, rather like the modern game of ludo.

GALLERY 11

THE SEA PEOPLES

And the descendants of Javan [Greece]: Elishah [Cyprus] and Tarshish [possibly Tartessos, Phoenician colony in Spain,] the Kittim, and the Dadanim. From these came the dispersal to the islands of the nations.
(Genesis 10:4-5)

This gallery surveys the peoples of the eastern Mediterranean in the second half of the second millennium B.C.E. The wall map to the left as you enter shows the patterns of migration and invasion that brought the great empires of the Late Bronze Age to an end. The various ethnic groups known to the Egyptians as the "Sea Peoples" spread throughout the Mediterranean region, settling in Sardinia, Sicily, Italy, Cyprus and the Levant.

Entering the gallery, you pass between two large painted clay coffins, made by the Mycenaeans, ancestors of the Greeks. The coffin on the right is decorated with running spirals, a floral motif and birds with raised wings, while the other is painted with blue fish.

The wall niche on the left contains contemporary pottery from Crete and Mycenae. The cream and brown-painted pyxis, or ornamental container (4), is from Crete and was probably used to store jewellery and other valuables. The large krater (5) bears a stylized palm tree design, which would have conjured up images of the exotic east. Kraters were used to prepare wine, which was so thick that it had to be diluted with water.

In the next wall niche are objects from Sardinia and from the cities of the Philistines, who settled on the coast of Israel. The Philistines were members of the coalition of Sea Peoples who attacked the Egyptian Delta in the eighth year of Ramesses III. The invaders attacked from both sea and land, and were beaten back on both fronts. Examples of Philistine pottery are shown here; several are painted with geometric designs in red and black. The lively little figures (6,7) were part of large clay vessels.

Another group of the Sea Peoples, the Sherden (Sardinians), raided the Egyptian coast in the days of Ramesses II, and joined the Libyan attack on Egypt during the reign of his son Merneptah. From the time of Ramesses II onwards, Sherden soldiers also appear as Egyptian mercenaries. They were highly skilled in metal-working — look out for the bronze figures of a cloaked woman holding a bowl (4) and a helmeted warrior with shield and sword (3).

In the pedestal vitrine neaby is the bronze figure of a Sardinian bowman (3) — the best-preserved example in the world. Wearing a characteristic horned helmet and carrying a bow which is almost as big as himself, he glares on the world with a fishy eye. Note the enchanting Sardinian bronze lamp (1) decorated with a mouse rushing around its rim, a dog gnawing a fox's tail, and two monkeys acting as lookouts. A larger monkey, conveniently placed in the centre of the lamp to support the hanging loop, looks on bemusedly. A superb stylized bull (2) completes the menagerie in this vitrine.

The glass case opposite contains figurines and pottery from Cyprus. You will need to enter Gallery 12 in order to see the pieces on the further side. The vessels shown here span over a thousand years, from the Middle Bronze

Age to the early Archaic period (1850-650 B.C.E.). One vessel is in the form of a double-headed ram (13), while others are decorated with fish (2), birds (6) and bold geometric patterns (1,9,10). A couple of jugs have beady eyes on either side of their spouts (2,16). Look out for the model chariot (12) with its two huge wheels, painted red and black. A bearded figure hugs a bird under his chin (7), and another bird, carved in stone, supports a bowl for burning incense (15). A small female figure perches on a chair (3), looking a little peevish; she has a marked family resemblance to the famous figure from the Philistine city of Ashdod. The similarity between the Cypriot figure and the one found in Philistine territory highlights the close links between Cyprus and Canaan in the Late Bronze Age.

Cyprus was a major copper source for the lands of the Mediterranean. The ancient Romans obtained their copper almost exclusively from Cyprus, and named it *aes cyprium*, "Cypriot metal," *cyprium* for short, which was later corrupted to *cuprum*, the root of the modern English word copper.

Painted baked clay sarcophagus; Crete, ca. 1300-1200 B.C.E., BLMJ 1235

Bronze boat; Sardinia, ca. 900-700 B.C.E., BLMJ 2889

The most striking object from Cyprus, in the pedestal vitrine just inside the entrance to Gallery 12, is the openwork cultic stand of bronze. Two sides of the stand are preserved.

One side shows a procession of four offering-bearers, the second carrying a metal jug and the last two bearing an oxhide-shaped ingot and a goat.

These tall, slender figures with fringed and belted robes are typically Cypriot. The other side of the stand shows a female sphinx. She has a lion's rump, eagle's wings, bull's forepart and a proud, angular human face.

Four-sided bronze stands were used to support large vessels, which rested on a broad metal ring soldered between the upper crosspieces. The vessels would have contained wine and other liquids; metal cauldrons could also have been placed here to serve as braziers. This stand probably stood in a sanctuary, maybe the temple of a god associated with copper production, to whom the Cypriots shown here are bringing offerings of raw and worked copper.

Look at the base of the struts and you will see that the stand was originally on wheels. Wheeled cultic stands were fairly rare, although we read in 1 Kings 7:27-30 that King Solomon had ten made for the Temple, decorated with lions, oxen and cherubim — supernatural winged creatures combining the strength of a lion, the power of a bull, the swiftness of an eagle and the mind of a human being. They may have resembled the sphinx on our cultic stand.

Returning to Gallery 11, you come to the last wall niche and pedestal vitrines, which contain material from Phrygia, Lydia (kingdoms in what is now western Turkey) and western Anatolia from the first millennium B.C.E. The kingdom of Phrygia flourished from the twelfth to the seventh centuries B.C.E. and in its heyday was ruled by the celebrated Midas, of whom legend told that everything he touched turned to gold.

In the seventh century, Phrygia was supplanted by the kingdom of Lydia, which fell to the Persians after its ruler Croesus, the richest man of his age, misunderstood the advice of the Delphic oracle that if he waged war on Persia, a mighty empire would fall. The empire which fell was his own.

Statuette of a warrior; Sardinia, ca. 900-700 B.C.E., BLMJ 2886

Figurine of a seated woman; Cyprus, ca. 1300 B.C.E., BLMJ 9

Fragmentary openwork stand (in Gallery 12); Cyprus, ca. 1200-1150 B.C.E., BLMJ 862

This buff and orange pottery is decorated with stylised plants and teardrops, ducks and leaping leopards. The jug with the trefoil-shaped top (8) was made especially for pouring wine.

The bronze dish (6) and spouted ladle (5) are examples of the fine bronze-working of the period; look out for the bronze lid in the form of a flute-player (7). Both this and another figurine (6) wear the famous Phrygian hat. These hats (conical caps with the tip bent forward) enjoyed a new lease of life in imperial Rome, where emancipated slaves wore them as a sign that they were free men. This symbol of freedom was adopted by the French revolutionaries of the late eighteenth century C.E. and can be seen to this day, worn by personifications of Liberty.

Two beautiful Phrygian vessels are displayed in the pedestal vitrines nearby. The first is in the form of a goat lying with its legs tucked underneath its body. Look closely and you will see a small spout between its front legs. Such vessels held wine, which could be released into a cup through this small spout by removing one's finger from the hole. The Anatolians were very partial to novelty drinking items and imported several different types of wine-drinking implements at this period. The birds and vines painted on the goat's neck, however, are Greek in style, and account for yet another element in the vessel's pedigree. The other vessel is shaped like a bull's head, and has small holes drilled through its nostrils, presumably for the same purpose.

GALLERY 12

THE ARRIVAL OF THE IRANIAN HORSEMEN

Lo, a people comes from the northland; a great nation and many kings are roused from the remotest parts of the earth. They grasp the bow and the javelin, they are cruel, they show no mercy; the sound of them is like the roaring sea, they ride upon horses.
(Jeremiah 50:41-42)

We now turn to developments in Iran and Mesopotamia during the late second millennium B.C.E. A people of unknown origins, called the Kassites, migrated to Babylonia at the end of the eighteenth century B.C.E., and founded a ruling dynasty there about 150 years later, inaugurating 576 years of relative peace. In northern Mesopotamia, the Middle Assyrian kingdom arose in the mid-fourteenth century B.C.E., and at roughly the same time the Elamite realm in south-eastern Iran reached its most prosperous period.

Turning to the first case on the right as you enter from Gallery 11, you will find objects from Babylonia. The stone fragment from Kassite Babylonia (5) is part of an archive copy of a *kudurru*, a stone tablet or large stela used as a boundary marker in a field. This fragment records a royal land grant and mentions kings Kadashman-Turgu and Kadashman-Enlil. Note also the splendid necklace of agate beads (6), inscribed with the name of the goddess Ninlil, wife of Enlil. Look out for the amulet in the form of a stylised crystal foot with ten toes (4), and the eye-stone dedicated by king Kurigalzu to the goddess Ninemush (8). Such eye-stones may have been used to decorate the divinity's garments, although most scholars suggest that they were set in the empty sockets of the divine image to serve as eyes. These gifts were given by kings and queens alone. The royal craftsmen carved them from carefully selected pieces of agate to produce a dark pupil surrounded by a white band.

The yellowish-white cylinder seal (4) is inscribed with a short prayer in Sumerian, which continued to be used as the "classical" language of religious texts and prayers, although it was no longer actually spoken. "O Nin-imma, great lord, merciful god who hearest prayer and givest life, have mercy on thy reverent servant."

Walking on to the next case, you can see material from the Middle Assyrian kingdom and Elam.

After the kingdom of Mitanni fell apart from internal and external pressures, the Middle Assyrian kingdom arose in northern Mesopotamia. The Assyrians now achieved independence and became a military power in the Near East. Aspiring to rule the world in the name of their god Assur, they began annual military campaigns to extend their empire in every direction.

The Middle Assyrian kingdom is represented here by a miniature mask (6 on the right), possibly of glazed frit, portraying a woman. Note the hollow eyebrows and eyes, which would have been inlaid (some bitumen, used like glue, is still visible in her right eye socket), and the holes for attachment. It may represent the goddess Ishtar. Next to her is a group of Middle Assyrian cylinder seals (1365-1057 B.C.E.). Note the splendid winged lion on the pink chalcedony cylinder seal, stepping out with tail waving, its crowned head held high. Later, in the Neo-Assyrian period, gigantic figures of such winged lions decorated the gateways of cities and palaces. Another seal, made of red chalcedony (3), shows the well-known motif of the Mistress of the Animals, a naked goddess clasping two animals by their necks. A clay cylinder (2) bears a royal inscription of Ashur-ketti-lishir, king of Mari, recording the building of a palace and citadel at Adalishhu, probably on the upper Khabur River in northern Mesopotamia.

The left side of the case displays material from Elam in south-eastern Iran, the home of a powerful dynasty that reached the peak of its glory in 1350-1110 B.C.E. You can see a glazed brick (1, on the left) from the huge ziggurat of Chogha Zanbil. It is decorated with a stylised lotus. A second brick (7) commemorates king Shilhak-Inshushinak I's restoration of a temple of the goddess Kiririsha at Liyan on the Persian coast (ca. 1140 B.C.E.). The inscription on this brick was repeated hundreds of times on courses of brick all around the temple.

Shilhak-Inshushinak's father Shutruk-Nahunte, the terror of his age, raided and desecrated the cities of all Babylonia and carried off its most important monuments as booty. Paradoxically enough, it is to his passion for collecting "antiquities" that we owe the preservation of Hammurabi's law code, Naram-Sin's victory stela and many other major monuments of early Babylonia, which were safely stored at his capital city, Susa.

The bronze figure of a woman praying with raised hands (5) is probably a suppliant goddess, like the earlier examples from Mesopotamia. She has no crown or flounces, but statuettes of

Elamite figure of a goddess; Iran, ca. 1000-800 B.C.E., BLMJ 2122

bareheaded women or goddesses wearing straight simple dresses, with their hands raised in prayer, are known from Elam in the early second millennium B.C.E. This gesture of prayer, with the palms curved slightly inwards and facing each other, is typically Elamite.

Also from this period is a unique Elamite female figure with clasped hands, originally part of the linch-pin of a chariot (4). One of her most interesting features is invisible — although her exterior is of bronze, she is modelled on an iron core that is the earliest example of this metal from the Museum collections. To her left is a tiny stone hedgehog (6).

The remaining cases in the gallery contain material from other areas of Iran.

The vast area of Iran is sliced by deep valleys and jagged mountains into distinct local cultures, some of them fairly isolated. These natural barriers prevented the consolidation of Iran into a centrally-governed kingdom like Mesopotamia or Egypt.

Although divorced from each other, most parts of Iran were open to influences from abroad. The Khuzistan plain of south-western Iran was basically an extension of Mesopotamia and had strong cultural and trading links with that area. Azerbaijan in the northwest was vulnerable to the influx of peoples from the north and east, and people from Central Asia could enter Iran through the region east of the Caspian Sea, galloping over the steppes (see the wall map on the other side of the gallery). Iran, like the rest of the Near East, was drastically affected by the waves of migration at the end of the second millennium. Around 1350 B.C.E., hordes of horsemen — Medes, Persians, Bactrians and Sogdians — from the steppes of Central Asia descended upon Iran to settle there. The culture of early first millennium Iran fused the nomadic traditions of these new invaders with local custom.

The Iranians enjoyed perhaps the most imaginative pottery in the ancient world. Examples are shown in the case to the left, beyond the map. Note the bull-shaped vessel (4), with his rump raised for the charge and his mouth opened to bellow. The smaller bull (9), by contrast, seems rather intimidated. Don't miss the curious bird with her head cocked on one side (2) and the human figure with a distinctly grumpy expression (3).

Another superb piece can be seen in the further pedestal vitrine, where an endearing if rather overweight figure raises a spouted vessel (like the actual bronze example in the same vitrine), as if to peer inside.

The other pedestal vitrine contains ninth- and eighth-century B.C.E. luxury items: finely carved fragments of tall ivory boxes decorated with goats flanking a tree of life, and to the right, golden rams' and goats' heads which decorated the rims of vessels.

An ivory plaque on the other side depicts two men clad in kilts. One of the pair has four wings. They seem to be taking part in a religious ceremony. This section was probably glued to a piece of furniture. This smoke-blackened fragment is carved in the same style as other ivory inlays from the palace of Hasanlu (850-800 B.C.E.). It was probably burnt when the Urartians sacked the city shortly before 800 B.C.E.

More items from Hasanlu, this time of bronze, are displayed in the next case to the right. The daggers (8,12) are typical of this site. Their handles were originally inlaid with bone, wood, leather, stone or precious metals. Note the elegant comb (4), repeating the "Mistress of the Animals" motif. Each of her hands touches a tiny monkey. Cymbals decorated with herds of deer running along the rim (5), a vessel with a long spout (3), a beautiful, lifelike calf's head cast in silver (7) and a diadem engraved with winged lions (6) are splendid examples of the elegant Iranian metalwork. Relief plaques (10,11) in the top left-hand corner of this case show mythological motifs — lions, faces and bearded men holding snakes nonchalantly in their grip, all gazing intently at the viewer. Note the woman's (or perhaps goddess') face with beady eyes, and the two figures with faun-like pointed ears on either side of a sacred tree (?) below her chin. The bronze cover (9) engraved with hunting scenes and birds is in the form of a Caspian Sea marsh turtle.

The case to the right contains a selection of the metalwork which the Iranian horse would have worn. Its bit might have been ornamented with ibexes or miniature horses like those on display (16). Its rider would have wielded a bronze or iron sword (7,8), and probably kept a dagger in reserve, perhaps with an ornamental hilt like the two daggers here (6). As the horsemen galloped down on the enemy, some of them flourished standards like the ones exhibited here (11,12,14,15). Bronze-working reached an extraordinary level of inventiveness and sophistication here, with animal motifs used to decorate a wide range of items: whetstones (5), armlets (3), horse bells (17), pins (18) and even cylinder seals (9). The "Master of the Animals", a male variation on the "Mistress" motif, appears again here (11,12).

Pottery vessel in the form of a person with a jug; Iran, 900-600 B.C.E, BLMJ 233

GALLERY 13

STONES OF ARAM

King Ben-haded of Aram gathered his whole army; thirty-two kings accompanied him with horses and chariots. He advanced against Samaria, laid siege to it, and attacked it.
(I Kings 20:1)

The black basalt reliefs of this gallery come from northern Syria and eastern Anatolia in the early first millennium B.C.E.

As the Hittite empire broke down, its regional princes founded independent local dynasties, known as the Neo-Hittite principalities, at centres such as Carchemish, Mazuwari (Til Barsip) and Hamath. The Aramaeans, a people of west Semitic stock, arrived in south-eastern Anatolia and northern Syria and founded small, independent states. In the mid-ninth century B.C.E., the Assyrians invaded the area.

Many of the reliefs are orthostats, carved ashlar stones which were set into the lower part of monumental walls. Some are purely Neo-Hittite in style, others show the influence of Assyrian art. Contrast the Neo-Hittite relief of the gentleman carrying a throw stick (on the wall to your left as you enter the gallery) with the relief of the two tribute bearers (on the platform to the right), which shows Assyrian elements — the men's short curly beards and long hair swept up in a bun. The man in the Hittite relief is more crudely carved and stocky, with detailed facial features.

Other monuments shown here are royal commemorative inscriptions, such as the inscription on the stone pillar in the middle of the gallery, set up by King Hamiyatas, king of Mazuwari. It records the building of the provincial city Haruha (perhaps modern Tell Ahmar in northern Syria). The text ends by threatening anyone who damages the stela with dire curses. On the reverse appears the storm god Tarhunzas, at whose command Hamiyatas built the city.

The texts are written in Luwian "Hittite hieroglyphs", a special script reserved for monumental inscriptions.

To the right you will see another god, standing on a bull on a large stela set on the platform. Bulls were symbols of divine power and virility for the Anatolians, as for the Mesopotamians. Offering trays, like the one behind the stela, were made in the form of bulls. The orthostat next to the tray shows demons carved in the shape of birdmen, lionmen and a bullman, with wings sprouting from their backs and ankles. The huge lion head snarling nearby is similar to those from Tell Halaf in northern Syria.

To the right of this group of sculpture with animal motifs you can see several funerary stelae erected to ensure food and drink for their owner in the afterlife. They show the owner sitting by a table heaped high with delicacies. The owner of the small limestone stela on the right even has a servant to wait on him. The most splendid of these stelae, in front of the window wall overlooking the stairs, shows a man and woman sitting together at table. He grasps an ear of corn, sign of fertility; she holds a spindle, the sign of female craftsmanship. Between them, a pile of flat loaves, probably rather like pita bread, symbolises the delicious meals they will enjoy for all eternity.

The nearby pedestal vitrine holds a rare eighth century ritual bucket from north Syria, decorated with six metal attachments in the form of bearded heads with birds' wings. It probably contained sacred liquid to be sprinkled in a religious ceremony. A similar bucket can be seen on the tribute-bearers' relief

Neo-Hittite funerary stela with banquet scene; Marash, Syria, ca. 950-750 B.C.E., BLMJ 1060

Ritual bucket; Syria, ca. 800-700 B.C.E., BLMJ 918

Orthostat with two tribute bearers; Arslan Tash, Syria, ca. 800-750 B.C.E., BLMJ 1111

and elsewhere in the museum, on objects from the third to the first millennia B.C.E. On the bucket you can see the sort of ceremony in which it was used. A procession of bearded men, girt with swords, carry branches and buckets like this one.

Next to the bucket is a stone pyxis, or small box, with a swivel lid. Two offering scenes are carved on it, separated by a building or city gate flanked by towers. The box is divided into compartments.

The next pedestal vitrine shows many motifs seen in this gallery in miniature form. The god riding the bull appears as a tiny bronze figure (4), there is a small bull-shaped offering tray (5), and supernatural beasts can be seen on the impressions from seals 1 and 2. The vitrine also holds a schematic clay figurine of a mother and child.

GALLERY 14
ISRAEL AMONG THE NATIONS

...We must have a king over us, that we may be like other nations.
(1 Samuel 8:19-20)

The gallery at the heart of the museum contains finds from Jerusalem during the First Temple period, which saw the reigns of Solomon and his successors, as well as contemporary material from Phoenicia, Israel's northern neighbour.

At the entrance to the gallery, you will come across a pedestal vitrine containing two models of Phoenician boats. One is of bronze and the other of clay. The bronze boat is decorated with a typical Phoenician pattern of lotus flowers. At its prow is a stag, whose pierced mouth may indicate that the boat was used for drinking or pouring some liquid. On the stern is a lifelike duck with wings outspread. The clay boat, which was originally painted white, is a more realistic model, with a bearded man reclining on one of the seats inside.

The gallery is dominated by the replica, two-thirds the original size, of a room from the gateway of the Ophel, found in excavations carried out by the Institute of Archaeology of the Hebrew University of Jerusalem (see the four wall panels around the replica). The name "Ophel" comes from the Hebrew word "to rise up". It was the highest strategic point in Jerusalem during the First Temple period.

The first archaeologist to excavate the Ophel was Charles Warren, in 1867. By digging shafts and tunnels, he discovered the outer face of two towers from the First Temple period. In 1967, Kathleen Kenyon dug a small square, exposing part of the smaller tower. In 1976, Benjamin Mazar brought more of the First Temple structure to light, without actually identifying it as a gateway. Eilat Mazar, his granddaughter, dug here in 1986. She identified the building as a gatehouse and discovered a royal storage building next to it.

At the beginning of the United Monarchy, Jerusalem was built in three parts — the hill of the City of David, the Temple Mount and the Ophel ridge linking the two. Later, in the days of the Divided Monarchy, the city grew much larger. David probably built his palace in the south of the Ophel. Solomon seems to have protected David's palace with a wall linking it to the earlier wall surrounding the City of David. He built the First Temple on the Temple Mount and next to it his own palace (1 Kings 6-7). In the ninth century B.C.E., in the days of the kings of Judah, the royal quarter was situated on the Ophel. It included the main administrative centre and a city gate complex. It was burnt down by the Babylonians when they sacked Jerusalem in 586 B.C.E.

The room reproduced in this gallery represents one of the four rooms of the gate complex (see the plan on the wall panel). This has been identified with the "Water-Gate" from the "upper house of the king" referred to in Nehemiah 3:26. The city gate complex functioned not only as a defensive feature but also as a place of assembly and commerce. Peeping into the gate chamber, you can see part of the plastered floor, bearing some clay bowls and lamps from this period. A storage jar, which might have contained oil, wine or water, leans against the remains of the floor. The wall panels set around the replica present the finds from the gatehouse — dozens of clay vessels, a small faience pendant in the shape of the Egyptian goddess Sekhmet, part of a

Seal with Ammonite inscription: "Belonging to Shual son of Elisha"; Transjordan, ca. 700-600 B.C.E., BLMJ seal 1099d

Seal with Aramaic inscription: "Belonging to Aḥitzur" (`my brother is my Rock'); ca. 700-600 B.C.E., BLMJ seal 1099f

Model of a boat (below, detail); Phoenicia, ca. 700-500 B.C.E., BLMJ 3005

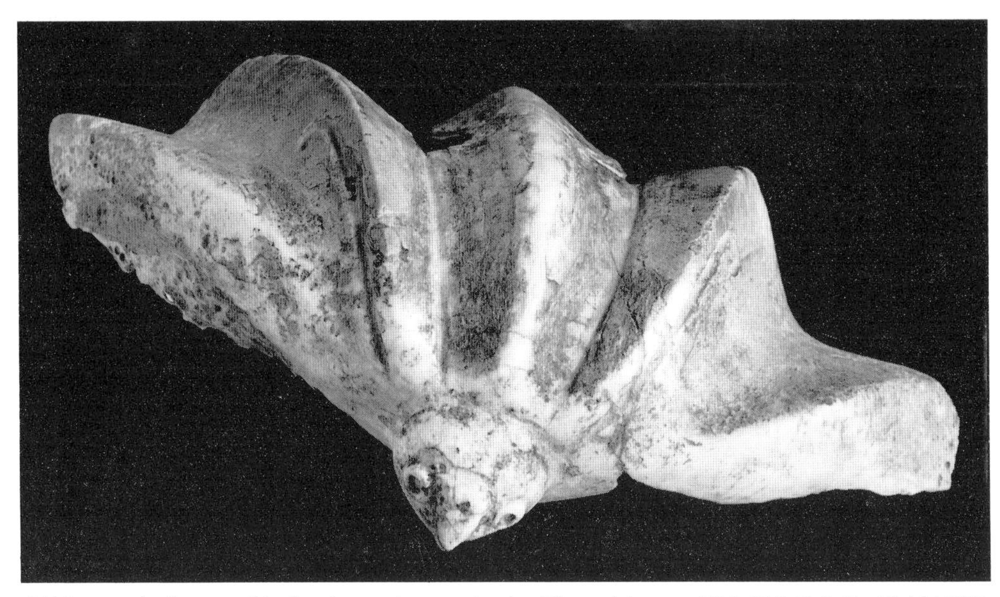

Tridacna shell carved in the form of a sea turtle; Phoenicia, ca. 700-600 B.C.E., BLMJ 551

duck-shaped vessel and a seal impression from a storage jar reading *lḥnh b/t 'zryh*, "(belonging to) Hannah daughter of Azariah". This is the first known example of a woman's seal on a storage jar. Maybe she held a key post in the royal adminstrative system.

Next to the reconstructed gateway is a large case containing three of the more than 40 pithoi (large storage jars) which were excavated in the royal administrative building near the gateway in 1988. One of them is inscribed in Hebrew script *lsrh'w...* "(belonging to) the minister of the O...", and another has a delicate palm-tree design incised on its shoulder. They probably contained oil or wine.

The wall case to the left of the gallery entrance contains administrative material in Hebrew script — eighth-century government seal impressions with the word *lmlk*, "(taxes due) to the king", from the regions of Hebron, Ziph, Socoh and Mamshit (5-10), and various seal impressions from the seals of well-to-do people of the seventh and sixth centuries B.C.E. (1-4). Look out for the scoop-shaped vessels (11), with palm fronds on the back of the bowl, and hollow handles shaped as lion cubs or a human hand holding the bowl. They may have been inserted into the neck of a container to serve as a stopper and dispenser for the liquid, which would be poured down the tube into the bowl. Two fragments of whitewashed clay figurines (12,13) may have formed part of household idols like those so fiercely condemned by the biblical prophets. The elegant little stone box with a lid (15) may have held ointment or cosmetics.

Seals which belonged to private persons during the First Temple period are on show in the wall boxes on either side of the gallery. They include one that belonged to a professional sorcerer (12, in the wall box to the right). Some of these ancient names are still in use, such as Elisha or Haggai. Others have been forgotten, and their meaning has become obscure. Look out for names which include the name of a god (theophoric names). Some are Israelite or Judaean, such as those containing the Tetragrammaton (the holy, unpronounceable name of God) and its abbreviations (-yah, -ahu, -ah and -yo). Other elements are common to Israelite, Ammonite, Ugaritic and Phoenician

Ivory plaque; Syria, Arslan Tash, ca. 845-805 B.C.E., BLMJ 2060

names, such as *adon* (lord), *hod* (majesty) and *shaḥar* (dawn). After Jehu's revolt in 841 B.C.E., we can see a clear-cut change in people's choice of names. During the reign of King Ahab, whose Phoenician wife Jezebel had introduced the cult of Baal, names such as Baala, Avbaal and Baal-nathan (3) were fashionable. Another example is the name Abdu-Baal, "servant of Baal", which appears on the ivory fan handle in the central wall box at the end of the gallery. In contrast, people born after Jehu's rebellion had names like Gadya or Shamaryo. Another name is Jonathan (2). This last seal is the only known example with this name — the Judaean counterpart of the Phoenician name Baal-nathan ("God/Baal has given"). This wall box also contains two very rare seals with the Hebrew theophoric element *tzur* (Rock); Aḥitzur (8) and Adonitzur (9).

The wall case on the other side of the gallery contains contemporary material from Phoenicia (modern Lebanon). The Phoenicians were the greatest traders of the ancient world, and in the tenth century B.C.E., King Hiram of Tyre helped Solomon build the Temple, sending him supplies of cedarwood, technicians and luxury objects. Here you can see an alabaster container with a dove-shaped knob on the lid (10), a cosmetic palette made from a shell, whose hinge has been ingeniously transformed into a sea turtle (6), and statuettes of the Phoenicians themselves (1-5). Look out for the sign of the goddess Tanit — a triangle with arms and a head — on two of the female statuettes (2). The urn from Sidon (7) was used for the secondary burial of a priestess of "Astoreth-of-the-Window" (Astarte-Hor), named Gerat-Molech. We know nothing about Ittobaal, who arranged this reburial — perhaps he was a relative of hers, or even the great king of Tyre of the same name.

The exquisite ivories in the three wall boxes at the rear of the gallery are said to come from Arslan Tash (ancient Hadatu) in northern Syria and Nimrud (ancient Kalḫu) in Mesopotamia. A plain ivory plaque from Arslan Tash (now in the Louvre Museum, Paris) mentions the name Hazael, maybe the monarch of that name whom Elijah anointed as king over Aram-Damascus (ca. 845-805 B.C.E.). It is not clear whether the Hazael plaque and these ivory decorations should be

Ivory plaque depicting a griffin; Assyria, Nimrud, ca. 800-700 B.C.E., BLMJ 2085

Ivory plaque depicting the "woman in the window"; Syria, Arslan Tash, ca. 845-805 B.C.E., BLMJ 2074

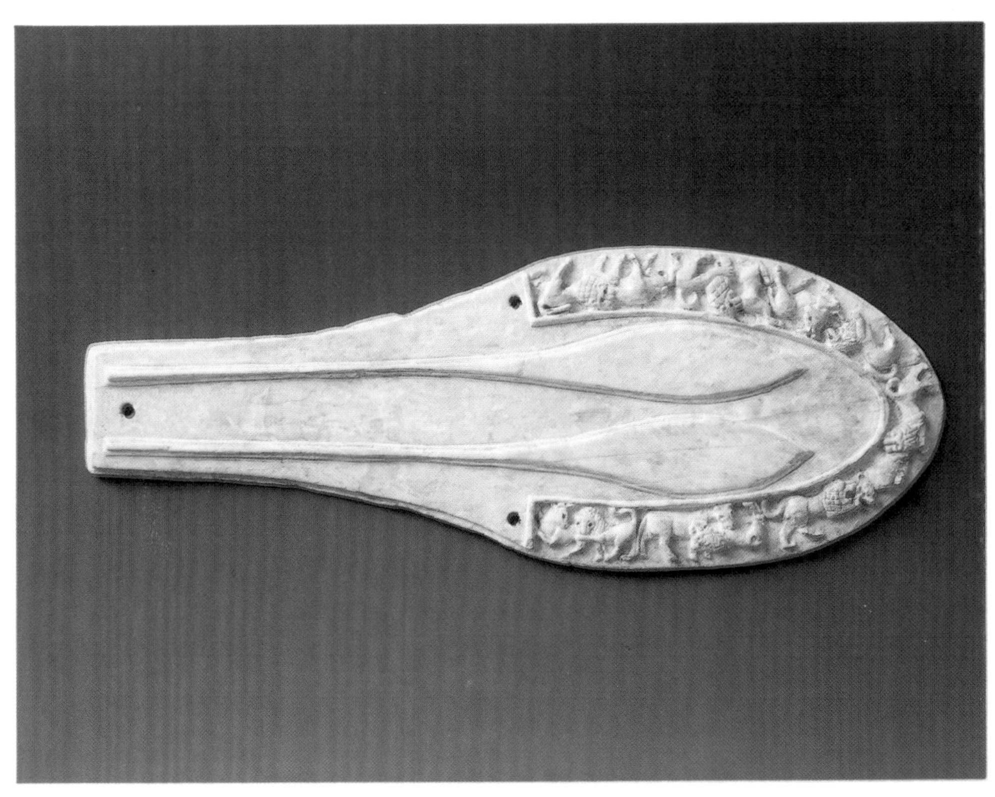

Ivory horse blinker; Assyria, Nimrud, ca. 800-700 B.C.E., BLMJ 2129

dated to the same period. Some scholars suggest that the inlays date from the eighth century, the time of Hazael's son or grandson. The Arslan Tash ivories were probably taken as booty by the Assyrians, at any point between 841 B.C.E., when King Shalmaneser III defeated Hazael of Damascus, and 732 B.C.E., when Tiglath-Pileser III sacked Damascus.

The ivories include carvings of a cow nuzzling its newborn calf (left box: 1, central box: 3-7), grazing stags (central: 1,2), and protective figures enfolding the baby god Horus within the shadow of their wings (central: 19,20). One of the Nimrud ivories represents a griffin rampaging amongst foliage (right: 1). Another piece shown here is the best-preserved ivory blinker from this period (left: 2). Its rim is decorated with a procession of miniature lions attacking bulls. This motif was very popular throughout antiquity — you can see it on another ivory (3) and on a small stone carving (4) in the same wall box. Nimrud was the capital of the Assyrian empire at this period. If these ivories came from Nimrud, they could have been sent there as booty or tribute, or commissioned by the king or his courtiers from an ivory-carving workshop in Syria or Phoenicia.

Note the motif of the "woman at the window" (central: 8,9), which recalls the story of Jezebel, who on the approach of Jehu "painted her eyes and adorned her head and looked out of the window" (2 Kings 9:30). Some scholars associate the "woman at the window" with the sacred prostitutes of Ishtar or Ashtoreth; others think that she may be an aspect of Ashtoreth herself. The columns of the window parapet are exactly like a set of small columns from the First Temple period which were excavated at Kibbutz Ramat Rachel near Jerusalem.

These plaques were originally inlaid with gemstones, and they would have been attached to wooden furniture, probably made of Lebanese cedar. King Solomon owned an ivory throne, which may well have been decorated with carvings in this style. Wealthy people also enjoyed furniture inlaid with such ivory plaques. The prophet Amos fulminated against the rich and callous "who lie upon beds of ivory, and stretch themselves upon their couches...." (Amos 6:4), participating in pagan revelry and oblivious to the misery and exploitation of the poor. These revels (*marzeaḥ*) had a long history, from the fourteenth century B.C.E. down to Roman times. They were celebrations, or alternatively mourning feasts in solidarity with the bereaved and the spirits of the dead. They entailed eating meat, drinking huge quantities of wine, anointing oneself with oil, singing to the sound of the harp and reclining on a couch.

GALLERY 15

ASSYRIA, ROD OF MY ANGER

Assyria, rod of My anger, in whose hand as a staff is My fury! I send him against an ungodly nation, I charge him against a people that provokes Me, to take its spoil and to seize its booty and to make it a thing trampled like the mire of the streets.

(Isaiah 10:5-6)

This gallery holds objects from two great empires: Assyria, which destroyed the kingdom of Israel in 722 B.C.E., and Babylonia, which conquered the kingdom of Judah in 586 B.C.E. The extent of these empires can be seen on the wall maps on either side of the gallery.

During the ninth-seventh centuries B.C.E., the Neo-Assyrians were the terror of the Near East. Every year their armies marched out to exact tribute, control trade routes and add new territory to the gains of the Assyrian empire.

In front of you as you enter is a stela showing an enthroned god and two priests, clothed in fish-robes and holding a cone-shaped sprinkler and a ritual bucket (like that in Gallery 13). This stela is unique; it is the only known monument of a *rab-shakeh*, or chief cupbearer. An Assyrian *rab-shakeh* headed an embassy sent by Sennacherib, during his siege of Jerusalem, (2 Kings 18-19). The *rab-shakeh* who set up this stela lived about a hundred and fifty years earlier.

Notice an unusual cylinder seal (22) in the case to the left of the gallery entrance. It shows the ruler of the Arabs, riding a camel to meet an Assyrian god. Most scenes on the other seals are religious — notice Ishtar, the goddess of love, surrounded by stars (8,11,13). Seal 17 is one of the most important seals in the Museum. Its decoration is arranged in two registers. The lower one probably shows a healing scene: a man lies on a bed inside a reed hut, with two attendants (perhaps priests). The upper register shows an Assyrian ruler seated on a wheeled throne drawn by two priests wearing high crowns.

Stamp seals came into fashion again in Mesopotamia, after an absence of two and a half millennia. An impression made by a stamp seal can be seen on a cuneiform tablet here (18). The stamp seals (3-7) bear symbols representing gods, such as the stylus of Nabu, god of writing, and the dragon and spade of Marduk, the patron god of Babylon (5). To the right of the seals is a clapper, originally one of a pair (1).

In the nearby pedestal vitrine you can see a unique statuette of a god carved out of a single block of amber.

The relief fragment with the horse in the centre of the gallery shows one of the many families which the Assyrians uprooted, just as they dispersed the ten tribes of Israel. This family is Chaldean and was deported after the Babylonian king Merodach-Baladan rebelled against Assyrian rule and was defeated by Sennacherib in 703 B.C.E. A youth leads the horse whilst his mother and a smaller brother or sister sit astride it.

The earliest king mentioned in this gallery is Ashurnasirpal II (883-859 B.C.E.). A fragment of his standard victory inscription on the wall to the left lists his conquests and the building of his palace at Kalḫu (modern Nimrud).

Part of an inscription of Sargon II,

Stele of an Assyrian official; Mesopotamia, ca. 859-825 B.C.E., BLMJ 1066

further along the wall, relates events of his second year, when he put down a rebellion in the Levant. During this campaign, Sargon conquered the kingdom of Israel and deported its people as captives.

After the Assyrians destroyed the northern kingdom of Israel, they attacked

Arm-guard for an archer; Urartu, ca. 800-700 B.C.E., BLMJ 772

the southern kingdom of Judah. Under Sennacherib, they conquered many towns, but Jerusalem held out and Sennacherib retreated (2 Kings 18-19).

A relief from one of Sennacherib's palaces (ca. 700 B.C.E.) on the same wall commemorates a battle fought in the mountains against the Phoenicians. On the right, two bushy-haired mountain soldiers fend off the Assyrian cavalry.

In the pedestal vitrine behind you, note the amulets of the Pazuzu-demon (900-550 B.C.E.), with his bulging eyes, lion-like nose and smirking grin. The amulet would protect women in childbirth from the attacks of demons.

The plaque in the same case (4), worn from use, was also used to exorcise the evil, sickness-bearing demoness Lamashtu, who menaced newborn babies and pregnant women.

The other side of this gallery contains objects from Assyria's rivals — Elam, Babylon and Urartu. The glass cases on either side of the entrance to Gallery 16 hold objects from Urartu, Assyria's major rival in the north from the mid-ninth to the late eighth centuries B.C.E. The kingdom possessed a large army. On the metal belts shown in both cases, the warriors of Urartu parade on horseback. (Enter Gallery 16 to examine the objects at the back of the cases.)

Men and women wore broad bronze belts, originally padded with leather, and ornamented with rows of leaping deer and fantastic creatures to protect them from harm and bring them good fortune. Look closely at the processions of fabulous animals — winged cats, goat-lions, sphinx-fishes and sphinx-scorpions parade happily along the belt.

The Urartians were also partial to elaborate bracelets or armlets ending in stylised calves' or lions' heads (left case, front, 4-5), and decorated hairpins or brooch pins (left case, front, 6-8).

In the same case as the belts are arm guards (bronze plaques to protect the archer's arm from the snap of the returning bowstring — left case, back, 5-6). One arm guard (6) is decorated with a god standing in a ring.

The right hand case contains pieces of horse harness, including a blinker (back, 4) and a T-shaped frontlet (back, 2). At the top of the frontlet is a royal cuneiform inscription.

Votive plaques (right hand case, front, 4-6) show a female worshipper standing before a god or goddess.

The pedestal vitrine near the right hand case shows a few items from the Neo-Elamite kingdom of the eight-seventh centuries B.C.E. In the centre, a graceful bronze bull (1) arches his neck. The bronze bowl (2) bears engraved animals and a man bravely grasping the tail of a bull, who seems to be looking round in surprise.

By the end of the seventh century, Assyria's power was on the decline. The up-and-coming power in Mesopotamia was that of the Babylonians, who conquered Assyria (614-609 B.C.E.) and built up an empire in Syria and Canaan.

In 586 B.C.E., Nebuchadnezzar of Babylon conquered the kingdom of Judah, sacked Jerusalem and deported most of the population of Judah to Babylon (2 Kings 24).

In the case to the left of the entrance to Gallery 14, small baked clay plaques (3) show a woman with a tiny child clasped to her breast, and a girl with a tambourine (6), wearing nothing but a hip girdle and a wicked grin, who may be a dancer. More musicians, playing a drum and a double pipe, appear on another plaque (5).

Many Neo-Babylonian cylinder and stamp seals show worshippers at prayer (16-21), adoring symbols and standards of their gods. A magnificent carnelian cylinder seal (13) shows a winged genie holding two birds and trampling a third. Two seals in this case (4,11) illustrate the method by which seals were often suspended. The fish-caped priests on seals 1 and 2 represent the legendary *apkallu*-sages, seven wise men who lived before the Flood.

GALLERY 16

THE LILY AND NATHAN SILVER GALLERY

THE SPLENDOUR OF PERSIA

And in the first year of king Cyrus of Persia, when the word spoken by Jeremiah was fulfilled, the Lord roused the spirit of king Cyrus of Persia to issue a proclamation throughout his realm by word of mouth and in writing, as follows: "Thus said king Cyrus of Persia, the Lord God of Heaven has given me all the kingdoms of the earth, and has charged me with building Him a House in Jerusalem, which is in Judah. Any one of you of all His people, the Lord his God be with him and let him go up."

(II Chronicles 36:22-23).

Impression of a cylinder seal in Greco-Persian style; ca. 500-450 B.C.E., BLMJ seal 727

In the mid-sixth century B.C.E., Cyrus, king of Persia, began to expand his country's territories. In 550 he defeated Astyages, king of the Medes, and became ruler of all Iran; in 539 he conquered Babylon and went on to establish Persia as the centre of the greatest empire of the civilised world, which in time stretched from Egypt to the Indus Valley (see wall map to the left as you enter).

For the exiled Jews in Babylon, Cyrus' rise to power was a sign of God's pardon. In his edict of 538 B.C.E., Cyrus allowed them to return to Zion if they

Stamp seal depicting a Persian spearing a Scythian; Anatolia, ca. 400 B.C.E., BLMJ seal 1148

wished and to rebuild the Temple and the city of Jerusalem.

We know something about the lives of the Jews in Israel and in Babylon at this time from the Books of Ezra and Nehemiah, and some of the apocryphal writings such as the stories of Susannah and Tobit. The Jews also appear in Babylonian cuneiform texts, and in the Aramaic papyri from the Jewish settlement on the island of Elephantine in Egypt.

Everyday life during the Persian period is quite well documented, including texts from Israel such as the Aramaic papyri from Wadi Daliyeh. Many ostraca (pottery sherds inscribed in ink, used rather like scrap paper is nowadays) have been preserved. The one in the first wall niche (20) is a letter from a creditor, giving details of a debt. Jews of this period would have been familiar with objects like these.

The seals in this wall niche were part of the administrative apparatus of the gigantic Persian empire. Their owner's name and title are inscribed on them, not in his own native language but in Aramaic, which was used as an international language by Persian subjects from Egypt to India.

Some of these seals are decorated with common motifs, such as the king overcoming two fabulous animals or rampant goats by grasping their horns, or the king shown as a mighty hunter shooting arrows (13-15, 22). Others imitate Babylonian cylinder seals, and are decorated with Babylonian or geometric motifs. Notice the rare Lydian seals with motifs from Greek art, which much impressed the Persians, such as a mare suckling its foal (16). Another seal shows a charming scene of an Anatolian

Scabbard tip; Persia, ca. 538-400 B.C.E., BLMJ 2119

couple (18). He rests his left hand tenderly on her shoulder, she raises a flower to his face in her right hand. Their other hands are clasped. Such intimate scenes are rare in Persian art, and were undoubtedly adopted from the Greeks.

Jar handles with seal impressions are also exhibited here, including some from the Persian province of Judaea (1-5). One of these impressions (5), reading "Motsa," probably located near the modern village of this name, was the trademark of wine from the estates of the Persian governor.

Look out for the coins used in Judaea (6-11) and the coin issued by King Darius, in whose reign the rebuilding of the Temple in Jerusalem was completed (6). Gold coins could only be issued by the king; other mints were restricted to silver and bronze coinage. One silver coin (11) shows a warship with a battering ram and a row of shields. Ships like this formed part of the navy employed by the Persians against the Greeks at the Battle of Salamis (480 B.C.E.).

Fire worship played an important part in Persian religion. The nearby pedestal vitrine holds two incense burners, shaped like miniature fire altars. The stone one is decorated with palm trees, two children riding camels, and animal and human figures, similar to the decoration on other incense burners found in Transjordan. The other, of gilded silver, bears typical Persian motifs, such as rosettes and four-pointed stars.

The wall box on the panel between the first two wall niches holds a rare fifth-century B.C.E. sword guard or chape, which was attached to the end of the *akinakis* scabbard. It is superbly carved with a magnificent bull's head. Note the palmette motif, which also appears on the silver fire altar you have just seen.

In the second wall niche, note the silken-smooth texture of the pure gold dagger handle (11), which was obtained by winding metres upon metres of hair-thin gold wire around the hilt. The well-dressed Persian wore his dagger stuck into the belt of his gown. He might also have sported gold and silver jewellery. The Greek historian Herodotus remarks that the Persian warriors, the crack fighting force of the empire, "wore torques and bracelets" (*History*, VIII.113). Here are some of their fabulous bracelets, ornamented with dogs' heads or rams' heads (5-7); rings shaped like snakes with jewels for eyes (1-2), gold and agate necklaces (8-10), golden earrings (4) and a silver perfume bottle (12).

Perfumes and oils were very popular with the Persians — note the alabaster ointment vessels in the next pedestal vitrine. The kings used perfumed oils regularly; reliefs in the palaces of Persepolis show attendants carrying a

Gilded incense altar; Persia, ca. 538-332 B.C.E., BLMJ 1339, gift of Anna Ternbach

Relief of a Persian servant with a wineskin; Persia, Persepolis, ca. 522-465 B.C.E., BLMJ 1046

cosmetic bottle and towel to King Darius for a wash and brush up. Queen Esther, like all the girls of the royal harem, had to have six months' beauty treatment with oil of myrrh and six months with spices and lotions before she was brought to the king (Esther 2:12-13).

Two relief blocks from the great palaces of Persepolis (522-465 B.C.E.), one on the wall, one in the next wall niche, show Persian and Median servants carrying provisions for the king's table at the great New Year feast. The Medians wear the usual trousers, pleated robe and laced boots, and a *bashlyk,* or scarf, wrapped round their heads and under their chins several times. Wine was brought in great wineskins slung over the shoulder (8), whereas rare vintages were carefully carried in small bowls (see the relief on the wall). Food was kept warm during the long walk between the kitchens and the banqueting hall in bowls under closely pressed-down lids.

Such processions of alternating Persian and Median servants decorated the stairways of the palaces of Persepolis, built by Darius I and his son Xerxes (Ahasuerus of the Book of Esther) and finished by Artaxerxes I. Even more fabulous was the palace of Susa (Shushan), where Queen Esther lived.

"For seven days the king gave a banquet for all people living in the citadel of Susa, to high and low alike, on the esplanade in the gardens of the royal palace. There were white and violet hangings fastened with gold and silver on a pavement of porphyry, marble, mother-of-pearl and precious stones. For drinking there were golden cups of different designs and plenty of wine..." (Esther, 1:5-7). The lavish descriptions in the Book of Esther give a picture of incredible luxury which is borne out by the awestruck comments of Greek visitors: "...If you chose to glance at the wealth, the luxury, the robes with sweeping trains, the anointings with myrrh, the attendant troops of menials,

Silver bowl; Achaemenid-Parthian periods, ca. 350-100 B.C.E., BLMJ 921

and all the other refinements of the Persians, you would be ashamed at your own case, at perceiving its inferiority to theirs" (Plato, *Alcibiades* I, 122).

Around the twenty-first of March, at the time of the spring equinox, the Persians celebrated their New Year's feast. The king's subjects brought him gifts with great pomp and pageantry. The king of kings received them seated on his royal throne and adorned with gold and jewels, and extended his sceptre as a sign of favourable welcome, as recorded in the Book of Esther.

The bronze and silver bowls decorated with rosettes (1-6) were probably part of the court dinner service. The king's servants gave him such items in tribute, and he in turn distributed them among the Persian and subject aristocracy as gifts.

A small section at the end of the gallery presents material from the Arabian kingdoms, which flourished during the first millennium B.C.E. Their wealth was founded on extensive trade in luxury items, such as frankincense and myrrh, used to make incense, and spices (see the wall map on the right).

The queen of the Sabaeans (Sheba) is familiar from the Bible, which describes her journey to meet King Solomon (1 Kings 10). The Sabaeans are represented here by a red agate seal in the pedestal vitrine (3), which is engraved with a jackal-like animal and a personal name. Next to it stands a stone bowl (1), probably used in some ritual and inscribed with a text in Thamudic, a North Arabian language. The wall panel to the left mentions Geshem king of Qedar, who probably appears in the Book of Nehemiah as Geshem the Arab; other evidence for the presence of Arabs in Judaea comes from an ostracon (2), found locally, which bears a list of names written in Aramaic script, some of which are Arabic.

GALLERY 17

HELLENISTIC DOMINIONS

Alexander of Macedon son of Philip... defeated Darius king of the Persians and Medes, whom he succeeded as ruler, at first of Hellas. He undertook many campaigns, gained possession of many fortresses, and put the local kings to death. So he advanced to the ends of the earth, plundering nation after nation; the earth grew silent before him... But the time came when Alexander took to his bed, in the knowledge that he was dying. He summoned his officers, noblemen who had been brought up with him from his youth, and divided his kingdom among them while he was still alive.

(I Maccabees, 1:1-4, 6-7)

The red backgrounds in the cases show that you have reached Gallery 17, which is devoted to the Hellenistic empires inaugurated by Alexander the Great. In 332 B.C.E., Alexander defeated Darius III of Persia and marched across the East, conquering most of the known world. (You can see his likeness on a coin (6) in the third wall niche, where he is shown in the guise of the hero Herakles.)

Alexander's conquest brought the lands of the eastern Mediterranean into far more intimate contact with Greek culture than they had hitherto known from trade alone. The wall maps to your left show how Alexander's empire was carved up amongst his successors, as well as the rise of the Roman and the fall of the Carthaginian (Punic) empires.

The Hellenistic culture of this period is represented by a number of beautiful glass (3, 10-12) and alabaster (2) vessels in the third wall niche. The long narrow vases are called alabastrons because their shape was copied from Egyptian vessels made from alabaster. These vessels were very popular as containers for precious oils. They were traded by the Greeks, Syrians and Phoenicians, and are found almost everywhere in the Aegean, Asia Minor and the Middle East. One of these examples was excavated at Nineveh; the other comes from the eastern Mediterranean, maybe Phoenicia. In the same niche, note the bronze figurine of a lion attacking a sheep (4), and the lead sling bullet (1) decorated with a scorpion, the emblem of a fighting unit. Piles of sling bullets of this type have been found at the city of Dor, on the northern coast of modern Israel. Coinage continued to develop during this period, reaching a very high standard of design and production; the fine gold coins shown here are decorated with beautiful miniatures of the goddess Athene's head (5-8) and a two-horse chariot (7).

The wall niche to the left displays objects from contemporary Egypt, ruled by the Greek Ptolemaic dynasty. The Greeks were only the most recent in a long line of conquerors who occupied Egypt during the first millennium B.C.E. Egypt was ruled in turn by its former colony Nubia (730-657 B.C.E.), the Assyrians (671-653 B.C.E.), the Persians (525-404 B.C.E. and 343-332 B.C.E.) and the Greeks (332-30 B.C.E.). Three crude faience beads (16) provide evidence of one of these waves of

Coin portraying Arsinoe II (below, reverse); Egypt, ca. 180-145 B.C.E., BLMJ 2022

Gem of a Ptolemaic prince with the attributes of Dionysus; ca. 225-200 B.C.E., BLMJ 2023

conquest: they bear the name of the Nubian pharaoh Shabaka of the Twenty-Fifth Dynasty.

In order to rule the country more efficiently, many of these foreign conquerors made radical concessions to Egyptian culture, and the Greeks were no exception. The Greek rulers were crowned as pharaoh, initiated public works and built temples for the Egyptian gods. Ptolemy I, first of the dynasty of Alexander's generals to rule Egypt, and Queen Arsinoe II are commemorated by the gold (12) and silver (9-10) coins in this niche. The tiny silver coins (4-5) were minted in the province of Judaea and bear the inscription "Yehud". A superb gem (3) depicts the head of a Ptolemaic prince in the guise of Dionysus. Amulets continued to be popular in Egypt: the examples shown here include two fingers (3) and a *wedjat* eye (14), which also appears on a faience plaque (7). Note the blue faience spacer bead (1), decorated with a scene showing the gods Horus and Re purifying the pharaoh, and a silver necklace counterpoise in the shape of the goddess Hathor (2).

Although key posts were often held by foreigners, the Egyptian upper class and administrators retained their power. Harnakht's family, mentioned in the inscription exhibited here (6), who held posts in the temple of Osiris at Abydos for seven generations, is fairly typical.

Between the first and second wall niches is a funerary stela from the Greek colonies in Anatolia. The dead man, Ariston son of Apollas, sits pensively on a chair (no banquet scene here!); before him stand a woman and child, probably his wife and son. A little dog paws at the drapery of his seat. In the right hand corner is a tree, encircled by a snake. These probably symbolise the tree of life and the immortal serpent, who sloughs his skin and "rises again". Two funerary wreaths, expressing victory over death and the hope for immortality, are carved above the scene.

To the left, in the first wall niche, you will see a range of popular Egyptian religious objects, such as the bronze figures of gods (7-8) which were donated to temples by pious visitors. These were particularly common in the Late Period (712-332 B.C.E.). The model shrines with the fish (10-11) might have contained a small mummified piece of the sacred fish as a relic.

The nearby pedestal vitrine contains a model coffin made of wood. On the other side is a figurine of one of the souls of Buto, a group of falcon-headed gods representing the royal ancestors.

The next pedestal vitrine holds a stela (2) from Carthage, Rome's most hated enemy, inscribed in the Punic script and carved at the top with the emblem of the goddess Tanit. It commemorates a dedication made to Tanit and the god Baal Hammon. The glass head (1) next to it may represent Baal Hammon. One of the Carthaginian gold coins (3) shows a lifelike horse.

Look out for the Judaean coins of the Hasmonaean dynasty of high priests (5-8) in the last pedestal vitrine, and coins of Antiochus Epiphanes IV (2, 4), the villain of the Hanukkah story. Another Seleucid ruler appears on a carnelian gem (10). One of the jar handles from the

Funerary stele; Anatolia, ca. 200 B.C.E., BLMJ 1052

Miniature coffin of painted wood; Egypt; ca. 600 B.C.E., BLMJ 332

Hellenistic period (9) is stamped *yhd* (Judaea) and another (1) is stamped with "Solomon's shield", the five-pointed star, and the name "Jerusalem".

The funerary stela of a young man casting his eyes heavenwards hangs on the wall to the left. It comes from Palmyra, known mostly for its celebrated queen Zenobia, who waged war on the Romans. This youth lived during the first century C.E., and was named Shamash son of Agilo.

The god Bes on a column; Egypt, 828-756 B.C.E., BLMJ 395

GALLERY 18

ROME AND JUDAEA

For the sake of Zion I will not be silent, for the sake of Jerusalem I will not be still, till her victory emerge resplendent and her triumph like a flaming torch.
(Isaiah 62:1)

Ossuary; Judaea, ca. 1-100 C.E., BLMJ 1337a,b

This gallery covers the period of the development of rabbinic Judaism and early Christianity. The right half of the gallery displays Jewish objects, mostly from Judaea, while the left half is devoted to Christian items, mostly from Rome.

In the centre of the gallery is a pedestal vitrine containing a few items illustrating pagan culture, which now entered its last phase. The face of Bacchus, god of wine, appears on a bronze handle from a wine jug, like the complete example to its left (3). The stone incense burner (2) would have stood in a pagan temple or home.

On your right as you enter the gallery are two small ossuaries ("bone boxes", 2-3) and a full-size stone sarcophagus (1) from the Second Temple period (1-100 C.E.). At that time, bodies were generally laid out in the family tomb until they had decomposed, and then the bones were collected and stored in an ossuary. As the corpse decayed, the dead person's sins would be expiated.

The owner of the sarcophagus apparently had ideas all of his own about this custom. On the end of the box is written CLOSED, and along the lid is a command not to bury another body in this sarcophagus. He seems to have been concerned that his bones should be ready for physical resurrection. The holes at the bottom of the sarcophagus allowed the body fluids to drain out.

In 66 C.E. the Jews revolted against their Roman overlords and were brutally repressed. On the nearby wall, you can see a photograph of the Romans' monument to celebrate their victory over this small, distant and determined nation — Titus' arch in Rome. The carving shows the procession of his Jewish prisoners, and the sacred and precious objects sacked from the Temple and now carried in triumph through the crowds of Rome.

The commemorative coins in the wall box (1-4) show *Judaea Capta*, "Captive Judaea", a mourning Jewess beneath a palm tree. Behind her looms the emperor Vespasian, leaning on a spear and resting his foot on a helmet. The other coins were minted at various Roman cities in Judaea after the destruction of the Jewish state.

In the nearby vitrine are relics of the First Revolt of the Jews (66-70 C.E.) and the Second Revolt, led by Bar-Kokhba in 131-135 C.E. You can see coins struck by both groups of rebels (1-4, 5-9). Bar-Kokhba's forces held out against the Romans for years in the caves of the wilderness.

The pedestal vitrine near the wall map shows representations of the

Sarcophagus with an Aramaic inscription; Judaea, ca. 475-525 C.E., BLMJ 1051

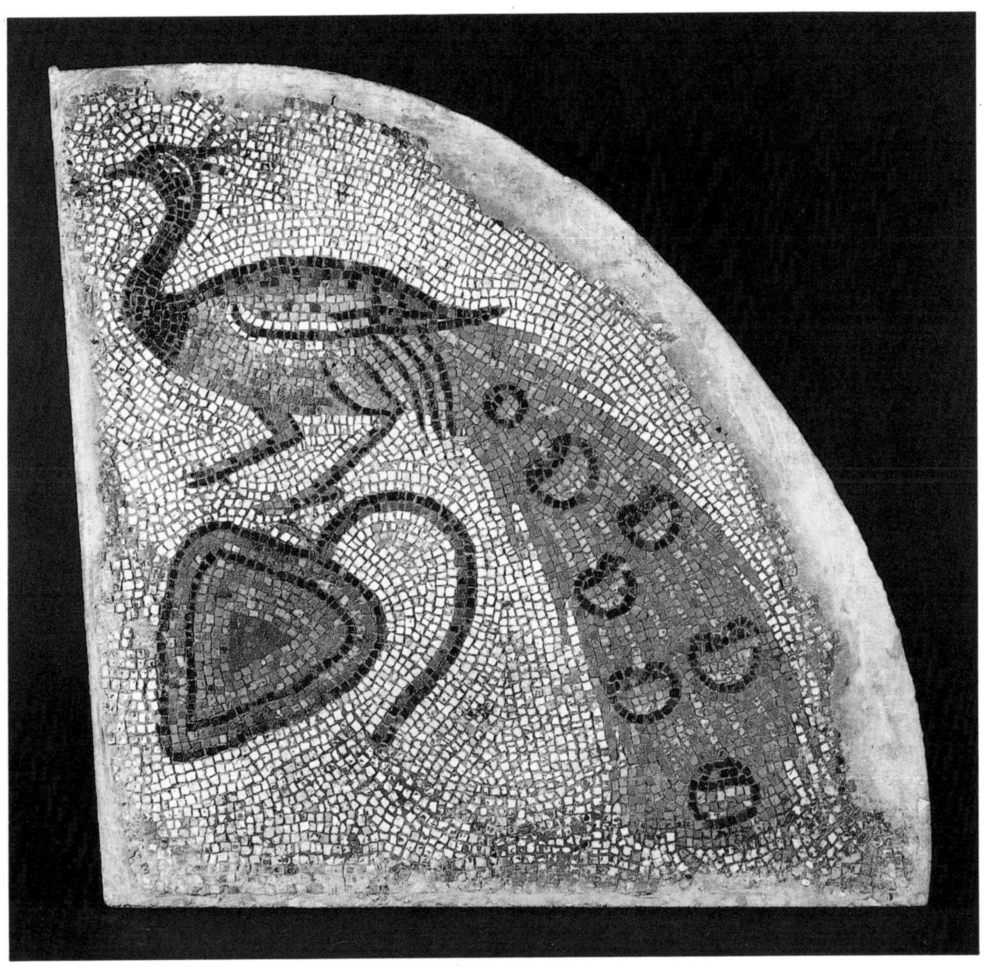

Fragment of a floor mosaic; eastern Mediterranean, ca. 500-600 C.E., BLMJ 1116

menorah, the sacred seven-branched oil lamp from the Temple. After the destruction of the Second Temple, the menorah was supposedly taken away to Rome by Titus and was never seen again. It became a popular Jewish symbol and has remained so to this day. You can see it here on a glass bottle (5), a fragment of a bracelet (3), a bulla (2) and a lead amulet (1). The seven-spouted lamp (4), popular from the late Roman to the Byzantine periods, may be a descendant of the menorah.

This vitrine also contains a bronze *maḥta* (incense shovel) from the second or third century C.E. When the Temple was standing, such implements were used to remove ashes from the altar and as accessories for burning incense.

The mosaics (fifth century C.E.) come from the eastern Mediterranean region. Walking from right to left, you will first see one showing an *aedicula* (shrine) containing a curtain, suspended from three rings and tied with a knot. Next comes a dog, perhaps part of a hunting scene, or a vision of paradise where birds and beasts frolic happily together. He is followed by a parakeet, his collar ends trailing, who has hidden between the leaves of a vine. The last of our parade of beasts is a peacock, a well-known symbol of immortality, resting on a gigantic ivy leaf.

The last mosaic, from a shrine in a church in Syria or Lebanon, takes us over to the Christian side of the gallery. It marked the grave of a martyr named

Sarcophagus of Julia Latronilla; Roman empire, ca. 330-340 C.E., BLMJ 1359

Julian, and expresses the hope that he will intercede for visitors to his shrine. Around 450 C.E., Theodoret, the bishop of Cyrrhus in Syria, wrote to his colleague Bishop Timotheus of Doliche, "...to this very day, when we approach the shrines of the victorious martyrs, we commonly enquire what is the name of him who is buried in the grave, and those who are acquainted with the facts reply peradventure 'Julian the martyr', or 'Romanus', or 'Timotheus'." Perhaps he knew the shrine of this Julian and had even read this inscription.

Turning to the left, you will encounter a huge Roman sarcophagus, one of the most spectacular of early Christian monuments. It belonged to a middle-aged lady called Julia Latronilla, who died at the age of forty-six, around 330-340 C.E. As a young girl, she would have witnessed the persecutions of Diocletian (301-309 C.E.), and seen her faith vindicated by Constantine's Edict of Toleration in 313 C.E.

The roundel in the centre shows her embracing her husband. Under it is one of the earliest representations of the Chi-Rho, or christogram — the first two letters of the word "Christ" in Greek, combined to form a popular emblem. It is surrounded by a laurel wreath, symbolising victory over death, and flanked by figures representing the sun and moon. Below are two Roman soldiers on either side of a cross, depicting the soldiers who guarded Jesus' tomb. The lid bears scenes showing Jesus' miracles: from left to right, his triumphal entry into Jerusalem (Luke 19:28-39), Zachaeus in the tree (Luke 19:1-10), the healing of the woman suffering from a haemorrhage (Matthew 9:20-22), the healing of the man born blind (John 9:1-39), and the fulfilment of Jesus' prophecy that Peter will betray him (Matthew 26:30-35). This combination of motifs illustrating Jesus' passion and victory over death and sickness is rounded off with a scene of Abraham's near-sacrifice of Isaac, seen by early Christians as a prefiguration of the Crucifixion.

Silver beaker for eucharistic service; Eastern Roman Empire, ca. 475-525 C.E., BLMJ 916

Another scene on the body of the sarcophagus (in the middle of the left side) shows God allotting labour to Adam and Eve — an ear of corn to him, symbolising agriculture, and a spindle to her, the sign of woman's craftsmanship, as in the Neo-Hittite funerary stela in Gallery 13.

One of the two pedestal vitrines nearby contains a silver chalice, probably used for the wine at the Eucharist. It is inscribed in Greek and Latin with the words "Holy is God, Holy the Mighty One, Holy the Immortal One, have mercy on us", and "O God, come to my assistance, O Lord, [hasten] to help me", phrases which are used in Christian liturgies to this very day. In the other vitrine you can see some Christian amulets (1-4) and a fragment of a ring (5), decorated with

Noah's dove holding an olive branch in its beak. A clay pilgrim token (6) — a souvenir brought back by pilgrims from holy places they had visited — shows St. Simeon Stylites perched on his pillar, where he remained for over 20 years, preaching to pilgrims and living a life of asceticism and devotion to God.

The last pedestal vitrine in this gallery holds a bronze oil lamp (2) bearing a cross, the source of spiritual light, and a bronze bowl (1) decorated with vine leaves, symbols of the eucharistic wine.

To the left of the entrance to Gallery 19 is the smaller of the two sarcophagi displayed in this gallery. It belonged to a girl called Octavia Bebiana, who died at the age of fourteen. Here she is on the left-hand side of the lid, with her hands raised in prayer. Her parents must have been extremely rich to provide her with such a lavish burial. They may have been a Christian family, but the symbols they chose could be purely classical. The sheep, for instance, might be the lambs of Christ's flock or simply a charming pastoral scene.

To the right is part of a church chancel screen, which stood in front of the altar, separating it from the main body of the church. It is carved with three crosses, the central one encircled by a wreath, and vine leaves. The Greek inscription records the date the screen was made and the names of the ecclesiastical officials responsible for its manufacture.

Incense shovel; Levant, 100-300 C.E., BLMJ 925

GALLERY 19

THE RACHEL AND MOSHE SCHOENBERG GALLERY

ROMAN AND COPTIC EGYPT

Embroidered linen from Egypt was the cloth that served you for sails...
Ezekiel 27:7)

Leaving Gallery 18, turn slightly to the left and you will reach the small corner gallery, 19, which records the growth of Christianity in Egypt. By now, Egypt had become part of the Roman empire, following the defeat of Cleopatra, the last monarch of the Ptolemaic dynasty, at the Battle of Actium in 31 B.C.E. The Romans saw Egypt as the grain-basket of their empire, and spared no effort to wring the maximum amount of taxes from an increasingly impoverished population. The Ptolemies had governed Egypt with the cooperation of the elite. The Egyptians now found themselves at the mercy of an arbitrarily imposed occupation, backed by Roman soldiers stationed permanently in the country, which drained its resources abroad to Rome.

Legend has it that Christianity was introduced to Egypt by St. Mark the Evangelist. Actually, the beginnings of Christianity in Egypt are obscure, but by the early fourth century it seems that about half the population of Egypt was Christian.

With the arrival of Christianity, the individual's hope of enjoying the afterlife was based not on the mummification of the body, but on the deceased's participation in the death and resurrection of Jesus. Over the first few centuries of the Christian era, burial customs changed radically in accordance with this shift in religious thought. Instead of being mummified, Christians were now buried wrapped in embroidered fabrics. Exhibits in this gallery illustrate both styles of burial.

The painted shroud in the long sloping glass case belonged to a pagan woman who lived in Egypt during the first century C.E. She would have been rather poorly mummified — embalming standards had declined drastically by this time — and then wrapped in the shroud. She wears a long white dalmatic (Roman dress) and plenty of jewellery, and she holds a wreath in her hand. The object in her other hand is not clear — it might be a fringed bag. As in earlier Egyptian art, she is shown idealized, in the prime of life, gazing serenely into the world to come.

Moving to the left, to the wall niche, you will see two wooden panels (8-9) showing the faces of a man and a woman who lived slightly later, he in the late third century C.E. and she during the fourth century C.E. After their owners' death, the picture would be tucked into the mummy bandages, over the face.

Some mummies of this period are very battered around the feet, and even seem to have been scribbled on by children! The archaeologist Petrie suggested that the mummies may have been kept around the house for a while, and that they were only buried when they grew too tattered to be presentable.

The luxury goods made in Egypt continued to be of superlative quality. The examples displayed here include a beautiful glass fish plaque which would have graced the wall of some Roman villa (10) and a piece of ivory furniture inlay (7) showing a podgy youth carrying

Painted linen shroud; Egypt, ca. 40-70 C.E., BLMJ 1097

Mummy portrait; Egypt, ca. 270-330 C.E., BLMJ 298

a duck. The blue faience bowl (6) carries on ancient Egyptian traditions.

The second half of this wall niche is devoted to attractive Coptic textiles (300-700 C.E.), of the type buried with Christians. After the Christian Copts abandoned mummification, people were buried in their clothes — sometimes in very elaborate garments, for in the fourth century St. Jerome and St. Basil complained that people were buried in rich clothes which would be better used elsewhere.

The textiles here were probably part of cushions or hangings associated with the burial. They are of rather too coarse a fabric to be worn as clothing.

Note that the motifs belong to Mediterranean culture, rather than being explicitly Christian symbols. Some of them may have been understood in Christian terms — the carnival revelry of Dionysus, god of wine, might now be understood as the heavenly joy of Christ's kingdom, or simply as a general reference to happiness and celebration. Other scenes visible here include a horseman with his dog (4) and dancing girls (1, 5), sinuously winding their way through an arcade.

After such cheerful and worldly scenes, it comes as quite a surprise that the Copts' most important contribution to Christianity was monasticism. In the late third century, people resorted to the desert to live a saintly life in solitude; often they gathered round a holy man and became his disciples, living alone but gathering together on Sundays to celebrate the Eucharist. Early in the fourth century, St. Pachomius founded the first monastic community. He gave this community institutional form by defining a set of rules for his followers. By the twelfth century, the monastic way of life had become so widespread in Egypt that, as the historian Abu-Saleh observed, "from one end of the country to the other you are never out of sight of a monastery".

Though Christianity was going from strength to strength, the last vestiges of the ancient Egyptian religion survived for a few centuries. The Egyptian goddess Isis, already very popular in the Hellenistic world, gained an adoring following throughout the Roman empire. She was a saviour goddess, sovereign over fate and fortune, who had the power to save her devotees from disaster, shipwreck and death. She was the "goddess of a thousand names", worshipped under different forms all over the world. On the far wall, you see the funerary stela of a couple from first-century Athens. The wife was a worshipper of Isis and wears a characteristic knotted shawl to show her devotion to the goddess.

The temple of Isis on the island of Philae was one of the best-loved shrines in the Graeco-Roman world. In the fifth century C.E., when all the other gods and goddesses of Egypt had passed into oblivion, Isis was still being worshipped in Philae and the last hieroglyphic inscriptions were written in her honour. Eventually this temple too fell into disuse, and, like so many others, was consecrated as a church.

GALLERY 20

SASSANIAN MESOPOTAMIA, HOME OF THE BABYLONIAN TALMUD

I will make you a light to the nations, so that my salvation may reach to the ends of the earth.
(Isaiah 49:6).

Footed silver bowl; Sassanian, ca. 500-300 C.E., BLMJ 331

Entering Gallery 20, we leave the Roman empire and turn eastwards. After the fall of the Persian empire, the Parthian empire emerged in north-eastern Iran in about 250 B.C.E., and proceeded to expand westwards to the Euphrates (see wall maps in Galleries 17 and 18). Their rule lasted to about 228 C.E., when they were conquered by the Sassanians.

In the pedestal vitrine at the entrance to the gallery, you can see a striking Parthian ornament from this area (2), a lively leaping panther with a naked man reclining on its neck. In the same case are a terracotta drinking vessel ending in an ibex head (1) and a small bronze mirror with a human-shaped handle (3).

The Parthian empire fell to the Sassanians, whose empire also included Iraq and parts of Armenia, Georgia, Afghanistan and southern central Asia (see the wall map). The Sassanians themselves were of Persian stock and spent much of their time in Iran, although the empire's administrative capital was actually in Iraq, at Ctesiphon, south of modern Baghdad. The Sassanians established Zoroastrianism as the state religion, but certain privileges were granted to the Nestorian Christians in Mesopotamia and Susiana and the Jews in Babylonia.

Many of the Jewish exiles in Babylon never returned to Jerusalem but remained in Mesopotamia and built up a flourishing community, whose scholarship was to rival that of Jerusalem itself. Other Jews may have emigrated

Incantation bowl with Aramaic inscription; Mesopotamia, ca. 400-600 C.E., BLMJ 3010

there after the fall of Jerusalem to avoid the Roman persecutions.

During the Sassanian period, the great Babylonian academies of Jewish learning and study flourished. Between the early third and the late fifth centuries C.E., these academies collated a commentary and interpretation of 37 of the 63 tractates of the Mishna, the redaction of the oral commentary on the Torah.

This Babylonian Talmud is a record of oral discussions about two and a half million words long, on 5,894 folio pages. Once the Babylonian Talmud was written it became the authoritative legal text and spread to all Jewish communities throughout the world. About one-third of the Talmud is *halakhah*, legal commentary. The other two-thirds are parables and fables. The text is a rich storehouse of information about the life, customs, beliefs and superstitions of both the Jews and non-Jews of Babylonia.

In the second pedestal vitrine, you can see silver bowls (1-3) from this period. One of the dishes has a fluted design (1) like the silver bowls from the Persian period, hundreds of years earlier. Notice the splendid bird engraved inside one of the bowls (2). The stone sceptre finial (4) shows the familiar Mesopotamian human-headed winged bulls, which were brought up to date by the addition of Sassanian-style headdresses.

Incised Sassanian bowl; Iran, 300-500 C.E., BLMJ 329

Another royal headdress can be seen on the gold coin of Shahpur II (9). King Khusraw II, who conquered

Jerusalem in 628 C.E., appears on a silver coin (7) wearing an elaborate winged headdress. Another silver coin (6) shows a fire altar, flanked by two Zoroastrian priests (Magi).

The mosaic panels on the wall represent the development of Manichaeism — a new religion based on a dualistic concept. The Good God, the God of Light, was believed to be attacked and captured by the Evil Forces of Darkness. The Manichaeans saw themselves as those who could free the imprisoned light. Manichaeism actively sought converts, and spread over a huge area from Spain to China. It lasted for about a thousand years, but Manichaean doctrines and customs can still be identified in later Christianity and Islam.

The first mosaic panel may represent Mani, the founder of the religion, while the second panel shows an angel with a halo and curious, horn-like wings.

In the last pedestal vitrine, you will see incantation bowls (400-600 C.E.) like the ones in the gallery of writing which you saw earlier in your visit. These bowls were demon traps, inscribed with spells to catch any evil spirit which might be lurking nearby. Such bowls were buried in the foundations of buildings, or under the threshold, to protect the house and the people who lived there. One is inscribed in Aramaic, using pre-Manichaean script (2), while the other (1), also in Aramaic, is written in Jewish script, proving that the Jews of Mesopotamia, like their pagan neighbours, were not above resorting to magical means of protection.

Sassanian coin with portrait of Shahpur II; Iran, 309-379 C.E., BLMJ 3160

MOSAIC COURT

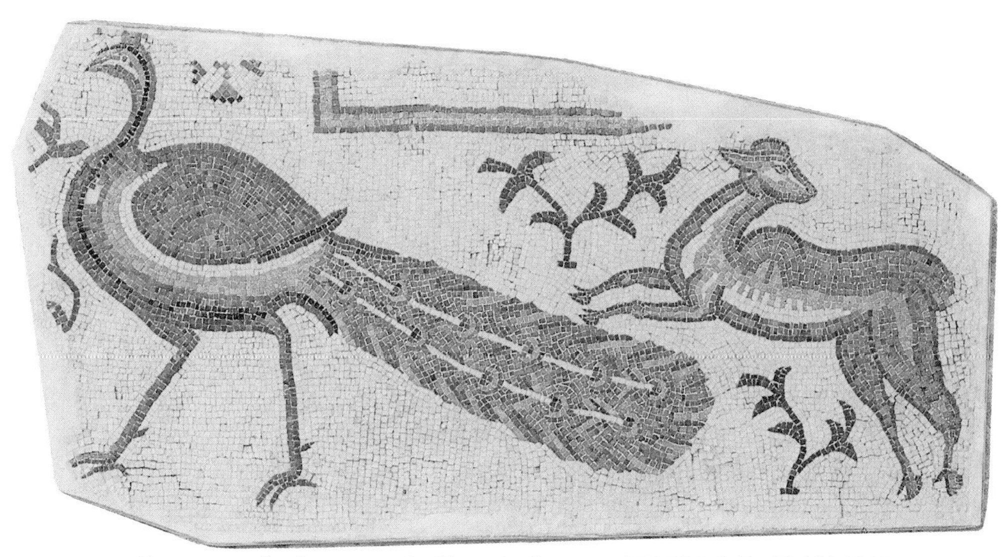

Fragment of a floor mosaic; Transjordan, ca. 475-525 C.E., BLMJ 1312

The courtyard contains a dozen or so fragments of Roman and Byzantine floor mosaics. Resplendent with birds, animals and luxuriant foliage, they transformed rooms into gardens of Paradise.

Some of the symbols are simply decorative, though others may have religious significance. Many motifs which were originally pagan, such as the vines and grapes, recalling the carnival of Dionysus, god of wine, drunkenness and ecstasy, formed part of the accepted cultural background of the Roman empire and were readily reinterpreted by Christians in Christian terms. For instance, the vines might symbolise Jesus, the True Vine, or the vintage feast of the kingdom of God.

In the central mosaic, a lion springs upon a bull, sinking his fangs into the beast's shoulder, a millennia-old motif which you may have noticed earlier on the Mesopotamian cylinder seals and the Phoenician ivories. Other mosaics show flowers and birds; note the rabbit gobbling fruit.

There are four different mosaics with peacocks: one is wandering in a field of flowers, while two others are at some risk from fawns frisking just behind their tail feathers.

For the ancients, the peacock was a symbol of immortality because of the renewal of its plumage. St. Augustine, writing in North Africa early in the fifth century C.E., notes that the peacock's flesh was proverbial for its incorruptibility, and remarks that a roast peacock served to him was still fresh after being kept for a year! (*City of God,* xxi.4).

THE CORRIDOR

In the corridor on the ground floor, Syrian mosaics from the third century C.E. depict the god Apollo, patron of music, and characters from the Greek epic of the Iliad, the saga of the siege of Troy — Hecuba and Priam, the unhappy queen and king of Troy, and the temperamental Greek hero Achilles with his beautiful captive Briseis, each labelled with their name in Syriac.

Fragment of a floor mosaic; Transjordan, ca. 475-525 C.E., BLMJ 1317

Syriac mosaic; Syria, ca. 250-300 C.E., BLMJ 1506, gift of Noriyoshi Horiuchi